SCHOLASTIC COLLECTIONS

Compiled by Ian Addis and Sue Spooner

Assemblies

© 1994 Scholastic Ltd

7 8 9 10 11   7 8 9 0 1 2 3

Published by Scholastic Ltd,
Villiers House,
Clarendon Avenue,
Leamington Spa,
Warwickshire CV32 5PR

Compilers Ian Addis and Sue Spooner
Editor Jane Wright
Assistant editor Sophie Jowett
Series designer Joy White
Design Can Do Design
Cover and illustrations Jane Gedye

Designed using Aldus Pagemaker
Processed by Salvo Design and Print, Leamington Spa
Artwork by Steve Williams Design, Leicester

British Library Cataloguing-in-Publication Data
A catalogue record for this book is
available from the British Library.

ISBN 0-590-53099-2

Contents

SONGS

PRAYERS

INTRODUCTION

Assembly assumes a uniquely important position in the daily life of a school. It is much more than just the fulfilment of a statutory requirement to gather for an act of collective worship. It also provides an opportunity for the school community to reflect upon the effective delivery of the whole curriculum by observing examples of work, participating in activity, sharing individual successes and reaffirming its commitment to an accepted ethos. Yet it is the fortunate teacher who consistently prepares to lead the assembly with undiluted enthusiasm. We are all familiar with the 'switched off' look so readily adopted by children when the material presented is perceived to be irrelevant, incomprehensible or just plain dull.

As Primary headteachers we are well aware of the dearth of published material available to complement the variety of functions listed above. We too have spent an inordinate amount of time in past years searching out appropriate stories, poems, songs and prayers at a level that is both identifiable and intelligible to the average pupil. Hence this 'Collection'. It contains a wealth of cross-referenced material providing easy access to a wide range of both new ideas and more traditional assembly themes that embody values and attitudes common to all denominations and faiths. At its heart are the key concepts identified with a child's spiritual, moral, personal and social development, with themes embracing five main areas: Rules for living/growth, Family/friends, Community, Environment and conservation and Celebrations.

A major concern has been to facilitate flexibility. The anthology can be used to provide a huge permutation of complete assemblies encompassing song, story, poem and prayer. Alternatively, each element is a self-contained unit which may be extracted to supplement additional or extraneous material if preferred. Assemblies can so easily become one-off, isolated happenings in the school timetable. Most of the material in this book is photocopiable, enabling teachers to make themes more relevant and meaningful by allowing children, for example, to read a story for themselves, to use a prayer as a model for their own writing or to focus a display around a poem. The benefits of photocopiable songs are self-evident, not least because they give children more immediate access to music and lyrics than they would normally have simply by listening and repeating.

Much of the book comprises specially-commissioned new material providing a refreshing change from the tired and over familiar. We have also included more unusual material which is, we suspect, not often found in collections of this kind. Not every teacher finds storytelling easy. Many prefer to read from a text and the stories chosen are all considered to 'come off the page well'. We are confident that this book will provide the busy teacher with an invaluable compendium of appropriate, interesting and relevant child-centred assembly material.

Ian Addis and Sue Spooner

STORIES

The story of light

It was dark ...

before the sun came.
The animal people
couldn't see,
though they had
heard the sun was
alive
on the other side of the world.
They met together in darkness,
bumping into each other,
stepping on each other's
animal feet;
and they decided it was
foolish
to keep living in such
darkness
when all they had to do was
take some of the sun
for themselves.

But which one of them would go?
Bear lumbered into the animals' circle.
He was eager to help his friends
and he never thought too long about anything.
'I'll get the sun,' said Bear.
'Wait just a minute,' said Fox.
'You might need an ounce
of my cunning. I'll go.'
But when he jumped up to leave,
two yellow eyes blocked his way on the pitch black path.
'This job is mine,' said Wolf.
All the animals cried, 'Never you, Wolf!'
Wolf was a wanderer. Once
Wolf got the sun, who knew if he'd
ever return?

Then Possum loomed thick in the middle of the crowd.
'I'll snatch a speck of the sun,' he said.
'I'll hide it
in my great bushy tail.'
The animals agreed that Possum should go.
So Possum walked east
to the other side of the world,
squinting with pain,
squeezing his eyes shut as the brightness
burned
and burned
even when his eyes were tightly closed.

He shielded his scorched eyes with his sweating paw.
And still feeling fire
and fear,
he came to the sun's spot.
His parched mouth said
O.

Possum stole a spark
of white-hot sun
and stuck if under his beautiful tail.
It singed his fur as he scurried
home to the animal people.
But when he returned,
the spark had gone out
and all that remained
was his charred
black snake of a tail, and ...

it was still dark.

Buzzard thought
he knew better.
'I'll keep that sun
far away from my sleek tail feathers,' he said.
He smiled a little,
secretly musing on
how much cleverer than
Possum he would be.
'I'll bring sunlight
home
high on the top of
my feathery head.'
And he left,
flying east
to the other side of the world.

He soon
snatched a bit of the sun
in his
big strong claws and
he placed it
on top
of his feathery head.

But the spark set a
feather on fire,
then another
then another,
and by the time he got home
there were no feathers
left on the top of
his head, only ash;
the spark had burnt out, and ...

it was still dark.

'Let me try,' called the smallest of voices.

'Let me try,' the voice insisted.
It was only Spider,
swinging above all the
animal people.

'You? You're too small,' said the bears.
'And too old,' said the foxes.
'You're a woman,' said the wolves.

'Never mind that,' called out Spider.
She swung down
to the earth,
took damp clay, and
with her tiny hands
she molded
a pot.
Then she walked
to the east, spinning
her thread,
and she followed
the rays of the sun
as they bent to lead her through
the shadowy grass.

Spider's pot first turned leather-hard
in the cool dark of her slow walk.
And as the day grew
lighter and hotter, so the pot grew
harder and drier.

It was a long walk
for Spider.
At the sun's spot
she took the smallest of sparks
to hide in her little clay pot. She
turned around slowly
and followed her thread
back to the west,
lighting her way
with the sun
in her pot.

And this was how
Spider
brought the sun to her
animal people. It's The
Story of Light ...

And even today
Possum shuns the sun;
he still has a tail with
no fur; and
Buzzard still has a head with
no feathers; and
Spider's webs still
look like sun's rays; and
pots are still dried
slowly in the shadows
before they are baked
in a very hot oven.

Susan Roth

The crow and the sparrow

Once upon a time, a crow and a sparrow bought a farm. They agreed to work together, and share the crops they grew on their field. One day the sparrow woke up early and called out to the crow, 'We must plough the land today and prepare it for the wheat.'

The crow thought for a while and answered:

'You go ahead, oh sparrow,
I'll put some gold on my beak
And some shoes on my feet,
And then I'll follow after.'

So the sparrow worked hard, but the crow never went to the fields. The next day the sparrow said, 'We must sow the seeds today.' The crow answered,

'You go ahead, oh sparrow,
I'll put some gold on my beak
And some shoes on feet,
And then I'll follow after.'

So the sparrow went to plant the seeds. She worked hard and she worked alone.

After some time, when the wheat shoots came out of the ground, the sparrow said to the crow, 'We must water our plants today.' But the crow answered.

'You go ahead, oh sparrow,
I'll put some gold on my beak
And some shoes on feet,
And then I'll follow after.'

So the sparrow watered all the plants by herself. It was hard and heavy work.

The crow never went near the fields to help.

As the days passed, the wheat grew tall. It turned into a beautiful golden colour. Soon it was ready to be cut. The sparrow said to the crow,

'Now it's time to reap. We must go and cut our wheat.'

The crow answered:

'You go ahead, oh sparrow,
I'll put some gold on my beak
And some shoes on feet,
And then I'll follow after.'

The sparrow flew away. She was sad and disappointed. All day long she cut the wheat. By nightfall, she had tied it all up in bundles. And she was very tired.

The next day the sparrow said, 'There are clouds in the sky. We must finish the threshing before it rains or the wheat will be spoilt. We must beat the wheat so that the grains fall out.' The crow repeated again:

'You go ahead, oh sparrow,
I'll put some gold on my beak
And some shoes on feet,
And then I'll follow after.'

For almost a week the sparrow worked day and night. She threshed the grains of wheat. And for almost a week the crow stayed at home and

rested. When the threshing was done, the sparrow said, 'Only the winnowing is left. We must finish it before a dust-storm blows our wheat away. We must shake the grain out of the shell. And the crow answered; 'You go ahead, oh sparrow, I'll put some gold on my beak And some shoes on feet, And then I'll follow after.'

So the sparrow went to the field alone. She separated the wheat into two heaps. One heap was made of all the rubbish – waste and shells. It was very big. The other was made of grain. It was very small. When all the work was done, the crow said:

'Today I'm in a mood to work,
I don't want to moan,
I know that selling grain is hard
So I'll work and I'll work alone.'

The lazy crow had done no work, but now he went and stood near the biggest pile. The silly crow did not know the difference between grain and chaff. Although the pile of chaff was much bigger, it was no use for eating. It was all the rubbish. The sparrow was angry. 'You silly crow,' she thought, 'I will have all the grain.'

When the buyers came the sparrow called out, 'Who wants to buy my grain? Grain for sale.'

Soon it was all sold, and the sparrow had lots of money.

Then it was the crow's turn, 'Who wants to buy my food? Food for sale.' Everyone laughed at him. 'Ho! Ho! Ho! Who wants to buy that heap of rubbish?' they jeered. 'Do you think we're so stupid?'

They walked away and he was left alone. He had no money but just a big pile of chaff. And then it was the sparrow's turn to say to the crow,

'Today you're in a mood to cry
But mine's a mood to laugh
We bought this farm together
Now you enjoy your half.'

Traditional Punjabi Tale

The pudding like a night on the sea

'I'm going to make something special for your mother,' my father said.

My mother was out shopping. My father was in the kitchen looking at the pots and the pans and the jars of this and that.

'What are you going to make?' I said.

'A pudding,' he said.

My father is a big man with wild black hair. When he laughs, the sun laughs in the window-panes. When he thinks, you can almost see his thoughts sitting on all the tables and chairs. When he is angry, me and my little brother Huey shiver to the bottom of our shoes.

'What kind of pudding will you make?' Huey said.

'A wonderful pudding,' my father said. 'It will taste like a whole raft of lemons. It will taste like a night on the sea.'

Then he took down a knife and sliced five lemons in half. He squeezed the first one. Juice squirted in my eye.

'Stand back!' he said, and squeezed again. The seeds flew out on the floor. 'Pick up those seeds, Huey!' he said.

Huey took the broom and swept them up.

My father cracked some eggs and put the yolks in a pan and the whites in a bowl. He rolled up his sleeves and pushed back his hair and beat up the yolks. 'Sugar, Julian!' he said, and I poured in the sugar.

He went on beating. Then he put in lemon juice and cream and set the pan on the stove. The pudding bubbled and he stirred it fast. Cream splashed on the stove.

'Wipe that up, Huey!' he said.

Huey did.

It was hot by the stove. My father loosened his collar and pushed at his sleeves. The stuff in the pan was getting thicker and thicker. He held the beater up in the air. 'Just right!' he said, and sniffed in the smell of the pudding.

He whipped the egg whites and mixed them into the pudding. The pudding looked softer and lighter than air.

'Done!' he said. He washed all the pots, splashing water on the floor, and wiped the counter so fast his hair made circles around his head.

'Perfect!' he said. 'Now I'm going to take a nap. If something important happens, bother me. If nothing important happens, don't bother me. And – the pudding is for your mother. Leave the pudding alone!'

He went to the living room and was asleep in a minute, sitting straight up in his chair.

Huey and I guarded the pudding.

'Oh, it's a wonderful pudding,' Huey said.

'With waves on the top like the ocean,' I said.

'I wonder how it tastes,' Huey said.

'Leave the pudding alone,' I said.

'If I just put my finger in – there – I'll know how it tastes,' Huey said. And he did it.

'You did it!' I said. 'How does it taste?'

'It tastes like a whole raft of lemons,' he said. 'It tastes like a night on the sea.'

'You've made a hole in the pudding!' I said. 'But since you did it, I'll have a taste.' And it tasted like a whole night of lemons. It tasted like floating at sea.

'It's such a big pudding,' Huey said. 'It can't hurt to have a little more.'

'Since you took more, I'll have more,' I said.

'That was a bigger lick than I took!' Huey said. 'I'm going to have more again.'

'Whoops!' I said.

'You put in your whole hand!' Huey said. 'Look at the pudding you spilled on the floor!'

'I am going to clean it up,' I said. And I took the rag from the sink.

'That's not really clean,' Huey said.

'It's the best I can do,' I said.

'Look at the pudding!' Huey said.

It looks like craters on the moon. 'We have to smooth this over,' I said. 'So it looks the way it did before! Let's get spoons.'

And we evened the top of the pudding with spoons, and while we evened it, we ate some more.

'There isn't much left,' I said.

'We were supposed to leave the pudding alone,' Huey said.

'We'd better get away from here,' I said. We ran into our bedroom and crawled under the bed. After a long time we heard my father's voice.

'Come into the kitchen, dear,' he said. 'I have something for you.'

'Why, what is it?' my mother said, out in the kitchen.

Under the bed, Huey and I pressed ourselves to the wall.

'Look,' said my father, out in the kitchen. 'A wonderful pudding.'

'Where is the pudding?' my mother said.

'WHERE ARE YOU BOYS?' my father said. His voice went through every crack and corner of the house.

We felt like two leaves in a storm.

'WHERE ARE YOU? I SAID!' My father's voice was booming.

Huey whispered to me, 'I'm scared.'

We heard my father walking slowly through the rooms.

'Huey!' he called. 'Julian!'

We could see his feet. He was coming into our room.

He lifted the bedspread. There was his face, and his eyes like black lightening. He grabbed us by the legs and pulled. 'STAND UP!' he said.

We stood.

'What do you have to tell me?' he said.

'We went outside,' Huey said, 'and when we came back, the pudding was gone!'

'Then why were you hiding under the bed?' my father said.

We didn't say anything. We looked at the floor.

'I can tell you one thing,' he said. 'There is going to be some beating here now! There is going to be some whipping!'

The curtains at the window were shaking. Huey was holding my hand.

'Go into the kitchen!' my father said. 'Right now!'

We went into the kitchen.

'Come here, Huey!' my father said.

Huey walked towards him, his hands behind his back.

'See these eggs?' my father said. He cracked them and put the yolks in a pan and set the pan on the counter. He stood a chair by the counter.

'Stand up here,' he said to Huey.

Huey stood on the chair by the counter.

'Now it's time for your beating!' my father said.

Huey started to cry. His tears fell in with the egg yolks.

'Take this!' my father said. My father handed him the egg beater. 'Now beat those eggs,' he said. 'I want this to be a good beating!'

'Oh!' Huey said. He stopped crying. And he beat the egg yolks.

'Now you, Julian, stand here!' my father said.

I stood on a chair by the table.

'I hope you're ready for your whipping!'

I didn't answer. I was afraid to say yes or no.

'Here!' he said, and he set the egg whites in front of me. 'I want these whipped and whipped well!'

'Yes sir!' I said, and started whipping.

My father watched us. My mother came into the kitchen and watched us.

After a while Huey said, 'This is hard work.'

'That's too bad,' my father said. 'Your beating's not done!' And he added sugar and cream and lemon juice to Huey's pan and put the pan on the stove. And Huey went on beating.

'My arm hurts from whipping,' I said.

'That's too bad,' my father said. 'Your whipping's not done.'

So I whipped and whipped, and Huey beat and beat.

'Hold that beater in the air, Huey!' my father said.

Huey held it in the air.

'See!' my father said. 'A good pudding stays on the beater. It's thick enough now. Your beating's done.' Then he turned to me. 'Let's see those egg whites, Julian!' he said. They were puffed up and fluffy. 'Congratulations, Julian!' he said. 'Your whipping's done.'

He mixed the egg whites into the pudding himself. Then he passed the pudding to my mother.

'A wonderful pudding,' she said. 'Would you like some, boys?'

'No thank you,' we said.

She picked up a spoon. 'Why, this tastes like a whole raft of lemons,' she said. 'This tastes like a night on the sea.'

Ann Cameron

Me and the baby brother

First thing in the morning Dad said to me, 'Guess what? You have a baby brother now.'

I said, 'I don't want a baby brother.'

He said, 'Well, you've already got him. Isn't that great?'

I said, 'Where is he?'

Dad said, 'at the hospital – with your mother.'

I said, 'Mum can come home and leave him at the hospital. That'll be okay.'

Dad said, 'That's no way to talk.'

So I stopped talking.

After a while Dad said, 'We are going to let you help name your baby brother. I would like to name him Tom, and your mother thinks Bill would be a good name. What do you think?'

I thought. Then I said, 'Let's name him Dustbin.'

Dad said, 'You are being very difficult.'

I said, 'Dustbin is a good name. Nobody else will be named Dustbin. Practically everybody is named Bill or Tom. Dustbin. That's a good name for him.'

Dad said, 'I think we'll do without your help.'

I said, 'That's O.K. with me. I don't care what you name him anyway. Hey, how about that? You could call him Anyway.'

Dad said, 'He's part of our family now. I expect you'll get to like him.'

I didn't say anything.

Then my aunt came to take me to a birthday party I got invited to before they sprung the baby brother on me.

She said, 'Isn't it wonderful that you have a baby brother?'

I said, 'Ugh!'

She smiled. 'Oh my, I'd like to be there when he comes home. What will you do when you first see him?'

'Hit him.'

Dad and Aunty looked at each other, and then they looked at the ceiling. Aunty said, 'You'd better get dressed, dear.'

So I got dressed to go to this yucky birthday party. I used to like birthday parties, but not any more. This one was awful. First they all got mad at me when I put mustard and salt and pepper on my piece of birthday cake.

'Why are you doing *that*?' my aunt asked loudly. She frowned.

I said, 'It's too sweet.'

Aunty said, 'Oh, I'm so sorry.' Only she didn't say it to me, but to the yucky kid's mother who made the gooey cake. Even with mustard and salt and pepper it was too sweet.

Then this kid pulled the cat's tail. So I knocked him down and said, 'Be *gentle*!' Why did they all get mad at that? You're supposed to be gentle with animals.

Then I tried to take one of the presents away from the yucky kid, and he yelled like a baboon. I said, 'Share! Didn't anybody teach you you're supposed to share?'

They took the present away from me and gave it back to him. After the way they always tell me *I* have to share.

Aunty said I was spoiling the party and took me home. Boy, I didn't care one bit.

Dad came home early from work, and we made dinner together. We had chicken and rice and green beans, and for pudding he made chocolate sundaes.

I said, 'You're as good a cooker as Mum.'

He said, 'As good a cook, not cooker.'

Cook. Cooker. Who cares? I was trying to make a compliment. I don't think people should correct other people's compliments.

I said, 'You know what I'm going to be when I grow up?'

'What?'

'A bird.'

'A bird?'

'A bird without any children.'

He said, 'Why do you want to be a bird?'
But he didn't ask why no children.

I said, 'So I can fly away.'

'From here?'

'Yes, from here.'

He said, 'You'd fly away from us, too?'

I said, 'I'd fly away so far, I'd fly away from *me*.'

'I see.' He sounded kind of sad.

'Well, I'd fly back. Probably.'

'That's a relief.'

After a while he said, 'Do you want to go to the hospital to see your mother?'

I said, 'Sure.' I waited for him to say something about the baby brother, but he didn't.

When we got to the hospital he said, 'If you want to wait in that room, I'll walk down the hall and look through the glass at – at the new baby.'

I said, 'I might as well come along.'

The nurse held up the baby brother for us to look at. Boy, is he *ugly*. I said, 'We'd better not call him Dustbin.'

Dad said, 'I'm glad you've changed your mind.'

I said, 'With looks like that, he needs a lot of help. Maybe you can call him Thomas William. Or William Thomas.'

Dad laughed. 'Maybe he'll get better looking in time.'

I said, 'I sure hope so.'

Mary Stolz

Spots

'Tomorrow is our school fete,' Mrs Bell told her class with a big smile. 'So don't forget to tell all your friends and neighbours to come along. There's going to be a very important competition – the Fancy Dress Competition.'

For a moment it was quite quiet because all the children were thinking what to dress up as. That gave Mrs Bell an idea. She gave out large pieces of paper and said, 'Draw a picture of yourself all dressed up for the fancy dress competition. Use your imagination.' Then she walked round looking as the children drew.

She saw two cats, three pirates, four clowns, five ghosts, a Little Red Riding Hood, a Buckingham Palace guard, a nurse and a cowboy.

'That's a smart looking cowboy, Alfie,' said Mrs Bell, looking carefully at one of the twin's pictures. Alfie grinned up at her. Then Mrs Bell's eyes rested on Jon's paper. Jon was Alfie's twin. There was nothing at all on his paper and Jon was just staring into space.

'Can't you think of a single thing to draw Jon?' asked Mrs Bell. 'Where's your imagination?'

'I haven't got one. Alfie got all the imagination when we were born.'

At that the class laughed their heads off.

'Nonsense!' said Mrs Bell.

'Guess what, mum?' said Alfie, rushing into his kitchen at the end of school. 'There's going to be a fancy dress competition at the school fete tomorrow, and I'm going to dress up as a cowboy.'

'Great! What about you, Jon?' asked their mum as Jon slouched into the kitchen.

'I'm not entering,' said Jon with a scowl.

'Look why don't you two go upstairs and have a rummage through the dressing-up suitcases. You never know, you might just change your mind, Jon.'

About fifteen minutes later, Alfie came into the kitchen and showed his mum what he'd found.

One pair of rather tight looking trousers.

'I'll put some tassels down the sides for you,' said Alfie's mum.

One bowler hat.

'I'll dye it brown for you and bash it in a bit,' said Alfie's mum.

One red velvet belt.

'You can wrap some brown paper round it,' said Alfie's mum.

One broken gun.

'I'll make a holster to put it in, then the broken bit won't show,' said Alfie's mum.

One perfect brown waistcoat.

'Perfect' said Alfie's mum. 'Now what about Jon?'

'He's lying on his bed reading a book. He says he doesn't want to be in the competition.'

'Well if he really doesn't want to be in it, he doesn't have to,' said their mum.

Just then she noticed Alfie's face was rather pink and his eyes looked tired.

'Are you feeling well?' she asked.

'I'm rather hot,' answered Alfie.

'Well take your jumper off then, love.'

As Alfie pulled his jumper over his head, his shirt and vest both rode up showing a nice, round tummy with five spots on it.

'Uh-oh' said Alfie's mum, lifting Alfie's vest a bit higher.

'Uh-oh' she said again as she saw his chest which was covered in spots. 'No fancy dress competition for you, I'm afraid love. That looks like chicken pox!'

Alfie's temperature went up. More and more spots appeared and he had to go to bed.

'Yes, it's chicken pox,' said Doctor Plant who came round a bit later to look at Alfie.

As soon as the doctor had gone, Alfie's face dropped.

'It's not fair. I was really looking forward to the fancy dress competition. I hate chicken pox and I hate everyone!'

Saturday afternoon was warm and sunny for the school fete. The field in front of the village hall was packed with people, stalls and games. The whole village seemed to have gathered there and everybody was chatting or laughing as they spent their money and enjoyed themselves.

'And now, ladies and gentlemen,' called Reverend Robinson, 'it is time for the fancy dress competition. Gather round ... There are twenty four children in the competition. Each of them will show us their costume and tell us a bit about it, so let's get started straight away. Number one: Jessie Bright.'

In her orange, baggy trousers Jessie climbed up on to the table where everyone could see her, and said in a loud, clear voice, 'I'm a clown. These are my grandad's braces and it took more than half an hour to put all this make-up on.'

Everyone laughed and clapped as she got down from the table. Then one by one all the children took their turn. The costumes were so clever. Some were funny, some smart, some scary.

'And our last entrant is number twenty four, Alfie Braithwaite,' said Reverend Robinson.

'Alfie's ill in bed. He's got chicken pox,' someone called out.

'No, he's not, he's here!' yelled Niashi, who was one of the ghosts.

Everyone gaped in astonishment at the sight of Alfie standing on the table in a pair of stripy pyjamas with the jacket buttons all undone showing a chest covered with spots. His face was covered in spots and even his bare feet looked spotty.

Reverend Robinson looked most alarmed.

'What are YOU doing here?' he asked.

'I'm Alfie with chicken pox,' came the answer.

'Yes, I know you're Alfie with chicken pox, but shouldn't you be in bed?'

'No, it's alright, I'm Jon.'

The reverend looked very confused.

'But I thought you said you were Alfie.'

'I AM Alfie, with chicken pox.'

The reverend looked absolutely baffled.

'But you just said you were Jon.'

'I AM Jon.'

'Oh dear, oh dear,' said the Reverend Robinson wiping his forehead with his hankie.

'Look, are you Jon or are you Alfie?'

'I'm Jon dressed up as Alfie. I've taken Alfie's place in the fancy dress competition. This is my costume. I'm pretending to be Alfie with chicken pox.'

There was a bit of silence then the crowd began to titter, to giggle and then to laugh and laugh. The judges were whispering together, heads bent, but as the laughter began to fade, Reverend Robinson cleared his throat and said, 'We were most impressed with all the costumes this year. We all agreed that the clown couldn't have been more clown-like, the bride was quite beautiful and the guard looked as though he'd come straight from Buckingham Palace...' There was a little scattering of clapping at that point... 'But,' he went on, 'Jon Braithwaite with spots and pyjamas looked so much like his brother Alfie, that we were all completely fooled, so we've decided that he should be the winner. Here you are Jon,' said the reverend handing Jon the big silver cup.

'Hurray,' the crowd shouted as Jon grinned happily.

Jon went into his classroom on Monday morning looking rather secretive.

'This is for you,' he said, handing Mrs Bell an envelope. 'It's something to do with spots.'

'Something to do with spots ...?' said Mrs Bell thoughtfully. 'Now let me think, is it a spotty handkerchief?'

'No.'

'Is it a spotty scarf?'

'No.'

'I give up.'

'Well open it.'

Mrs Bell opened the envelope and unfolded the large piece of paper inside. She held it up for all the class to see. It was a picture of Jon, (or was it Alfie!) in pyjamas and spots.

'Thank you, Jon, you turned out to have the biggest imagination of all,' said Mrs Bell as she stuck the picture up with the others. 'And now,' she went on, 'I've got a surprise for you. It's something to do with spots.'

Jon looked quite blank. He had no idea what it could be.

'I know,' said Jessie.

'I know,' said all the class.

'I give up,' said Jon. So Mrs Bell took him to look in the mirror on her table. Jon looked. His face was covered with spots.

'Oh NO!' he said, 'Not me TOO!'

Ann Bryant

The box

My mother was at a meeting. And my father had an errand to do.

'Will you kids be all right till I get back?' he asked.

'Yes,' we said.

'Fine,' my father said. 'I may have a surprise for you.'

'Great!' I said.

My dad left.

'I wonder what your surprise will be,' Gloria said.

'Me too,' Huey and I said, both at the same time.

The three of us stayed in the garden, taking turns swing-jumping. We didn't hear my dad coming back. It started getting dark and hard to see.

'I jumped farther than you,' Huey said.

'You didn't,' I said.

'Did too,' Huey said.

'Did not, bean sprout,' I said.

'Did not, WHAT?' my father said. He *had* come home. He was on the porch.

'Just *did not* was all I said.'

'He called me "bean sprout"!' Huey shouted.

'BEAN SPROUT!' my father roared. 'He called you BEAN SPROUT?'

'I think I'll be going home now,' Gloria said, very softly. She was already in the shadows, half-way out of the garden.

My father stepped out of the porch door. He put down a big cardboard box he was carrying.

'Wait a minute, Gloria,' my father said. 'I'd like you to stay. I have something in mind for these boys!'

I looked at Huey. 'We can forget the surprise,' I whispered.

'A surprise is coming,' Huey whispered back. 'But it won't be nice.'

We all followed my father into the house.

'Are you going to send us to our room?' I asked.

'No,' my father said. He had a scary smile.

'Are you going to make us wash windows?' Huey asked.

'No,' my father said. He smiled again, like a tiger.

'What *are* you going to do?' Gloria asked.

'I have an idea about these boys, Gloria,' my father said, just like he and Gloria were best friends. 'I think they need to go through a potentially dangerous situation together. Then they may like each other more.'

'What do you mean, a "potentially dangerous situation"?' I said.

'I mean one that *could* be dangerous if you don't handle it right.' My father smiled again, like a cobra.

'Like what?' Huey said.

'I know you boys like animals,' my father said. 'It wouldn't be anything much. Something like – live alligators. Maybe – sharks.'

'Sharks!' Huey said. He reached for my hand.

'Now you boys make yourselves comfortable,' my father said. 'Gloria and I will be back in a minute.'

The two of them walked outside to the porch. Gloria looked back at us. Her eyes said good-bye forever.

Huey and I sat on the couch.

'Is Gloria going to help carry in the sharks?' he asked.

'I don't know!' I said. 'Huey, I'm sorry I called you 'bean sprout'.'

'That's O.K.,' Huey said.

'It's taking them a long time,' I said.

We waited. Huey started rubbing his special laser ring that is supposed to fry your enemies to a crisp, although actually it couldn't even fry an egg.

Gloria and my father came back. They had the cardboard box my father had left on the porch.

'Hold it level, Gloria,' my father said.

Inside the package something skittered.

'Not sharks,' Huey whispered to me. 'Maybe – live snakes!'

Gloria and my father set the box down in front of us. It was tied with strong cord. I moved my feet away from it.

'Now your job,' my father said to us, 'will be to open this box.'

'O.K.,' Huey said, rubbing his ring.

'I don't want to,' I said.

Gloria looked at me sympathetically. Even my father looked a little bit sorry.

'I don't want you to go into this without a fighting chance,' he said. 'Wait a minute.'

He went into the kitchen.

I looked at the box. I tried to sense what was inside it. All I could sense was darkness. And breathing.

'Gloria,' I whispered quickly, 'do you know what's inside there? Would you say it's really dangerous?'

'I would say' – Gloria began – 'that if I were you, I would say my prayers.'

'Well, here you are,' my father said cheerily.

He was carrying two kitchen knives.

I started making a plan. Huey and I could stab the box to shreds. Afterwards, we could find out what *had been* inside. I picked up one of the knives.

'Sorry,' my father said. 'The knives are for later. You have to open the box with your bare hands.'

'With our bare hands?' Huey repeated. He didn't look so brave any more.

'Right!' my father said. 'And be gentle. That's a good box. I may want to use it again.'

'Couldn't this wait until tomorrow?' I said. Sometimes my father gets over his strange ideas in a day or so.

My father smiled his tiger-cobra smile. He raised his eyebrows.

'No,' he said. 'But I'll help you a little.'

He took one of the knives and cut the cord on the box. That left only a little piece of tape on the top between whatever it was and us.

'Can't you tell us *anything* about what's in there?' I said.

'Just this,' my father said. 'They're hungry!'

Whatever it was, there was more than one!

'Come on, Julian,' Huey said. He was rubbing his laser ring.

'Ready,' I said.

We each took hold of one top flap of the box. We pulled in opposite

directions so hard we fell on the floor. Nothing came out of the box at us.

We got up. We moved closer to the box.

'It's the surprise!' Huey said.

In one corner of the box were two baby rabbits. They blinked in the light. Their long ears trembled. One was brown. One was white.

Huey put his hand into the box. The white one smelled it.

'They're brothers,' my father said, 'and they're hungry.'

Huey picked up the white one and held it in his hands.

I picked up the brown one.

'You said they were dangerous,' I said.

'Could be,' my father said. 'If you boys don't take those knives and cut them some lettuce and carrots, they might start nibbling your shirts.'

So we cut up lettuce and carrots while Gloria held the rabbits.

'Well, what about names?' my father said.

I thought of the toughest name for a rabbit I could. 'Mine is Jake,' I said.

'And what about you, Huey?' my father asked.

'Wait a minute. I have to think,' Huey answered. He shut his eyes.

In a minute he opened them. He didn't say anything.

My father said, 'Come on, Huey. What is it? Tell us.'

A big grin spread across Huey's face.

'Bean sprout,' he said.

Ann Cameron

Timothy's new ears

'My big brother's got dog's ears,' Lee said to Natasha as they walked to school.

Natasha giggled. 'Are they long and floppy, like a spaniel's ears?'

'Yes, they are,' said Lee. 'They're long and floppy. And they're black and white. And not only are they *like* a spaniel's ears, they *are* a spaniels ears. They're part of a spaniel called Scamp.'

Lee's brother, Timothy, was deaf, and Scamp was his special Hearing Dog. She had been trained to listen for sound which Timothy couldn't hear, like the doorbell ringing or his alarm clock. She was his ears.

After school Natasha went home with Lee to see Scamp. As they walked in the door Scamp came running to meet them. She loved company.

Through the open kitchen door they could see Timothy. He was sitting at the table looking at the job adverts in the local paper. He hadn't heard them come into the house because of his deafness. But when Scamp ran up to him and pulled gently at his trouser leg with her teeth, he looked up and saw them.

'Hi!' he said.

Lee stood in front of Timothy and said, 'I've brought Natasha to meet Scamp. OK?'

Timothy smiled. 'OK!' he said. Lee knew how to speak clearly and slowly so that Timothy could tell what she was saying by watching her lips, although he couldn't hear the words.

Scamp sat down beside Timothy's chair, resting her chin on the edge of the seat. Timothy stroked the top of her curly head and she looked up at him with her dark brown eyes.

'Hey, she loves you.' Natasha spoke carefully too, and Timothy nodded and smiled.

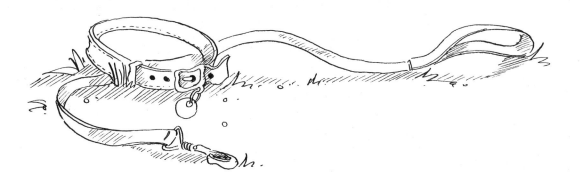

But Natasha looked worried when she turned to Lee. 'We just walked into the house, Lee. We didn't have to ring the bell. What would happen if you'd forgotten your key?'

'I'd ring the bell,' said Lee. 'When Scamp heard it she'd run to Timothy and pull at his trouser leg and lead him to the door. And when Timothy saw it was me, he'd let me in.'

When Natasha got home she told her mum and dad about Scamp, and how clever she was.

Natasha's dad was really pleased to hear the news. He said Timothy had been waiting for months to get Scamp from Hearing Dogs for the Deaf. 'They arrange everything, but there's always a waiting list. Some of the dogs are strays, but wherever they come from they need about four months training. Then Timothy and Scamp would have to get to know each other.'

Natasha said, 'Scamp loves Timothy. You can see it in her eyes.'

Well, yes,' said her dad, 'but that's not enough. Scamp had to learn how to be obedient too – to do what Timothy needs her to do, like listen for the door bell. And Timothy hasn't had a dog before, so he had to learn how to look after Scamp.'

At the weekend Natasha and her dad saw Timothy and Scamp out walking. To Natasha's surprise, Scamp was wearing a bright yellowy-orange coat strapped round her body. It had HEARING DOG FOR THE DEAF written on it. The colour matched her collar and lead.

'She's very smart,' Natasha said to Timothy.

'The coat lets people know I'm deaf,' Timothy explained. 'I never went out on my own before I got Scamp, but now we enjoy our walks, don't we girl?'

Scamp wagged her tail and lifted up a front paw for Timothy to shake. Natasha looked longingly at Scamp and thought how lucky Timothy was to have such a lovely dog; then she remembered how lucky she was to be able to hear.

Anne English

The miraculous Orange Tree

Joey lived in a house in the middle of a large city. There was a small space at the back of Joey's house which could not rightly be called a garden as there was no lawn and no flower-beds. The space was all covered over in concrete and they called it the backyard. It was quite good for playing ball or riding a bicycle round and round when the weather was dry; but when it rained, Joey would watch the raindrops bouncing on the grey stone and he wondered if he would ever see the place he had heard his mother and father talk about. They had seen a place which was always sunny – where there was plenty of space, sea – and orange trees! There were few trees where Joey lived – apart from those in the park – and he could hardly imagine what an orange tree looked like.

One morning Joey woke early. It was summer and sun was shining. From his bed, Joey could see a chink of bright, blue sky through the curtains. He jumped up and ran to look out of the window. As he drew the curtains – what a sight met his eyes! There standing in the middle of the backyard was – an Orange Tree!

Joey thought he must still be asleep. He turned his back, shut his eyes and counted to ten; then he looked again. It was still there. An Orange Tree. There was no doubt about it, for it was laden with oranges.

Joey ran to his parents' room. His mother and father were still asleep.

'Ma! Pa!' cried Joey.

'Go away, we're still sleeping,' groaned Pa.

'There's an Orange Tree in our backyard,' said Joey, shaking his Ma.

"It's another of your dreams, Joey, now go away and don't be a nuisance.'

Joey ran to the window. Yes it was still there.

'I'm not dreaming, Ma, I can see it from your window too – oh please come and look!' begged Joey.

Pa snorted and pulled the bedclothes over his ears. Ma sighed, 'Joey, now don't go and get your Pa and me all mad. Go away and play.'

She rolled over and pulled the bedclothes up over her ears.

Joey's grandfather lived with them. So Joey ran to him.

'Grandfather, Grandfather! Have you seen the Orange Tree in our backyard?'

'Are you making up stories again, Joey?' asked Grandfather sternly.

Joey begged his grandfather just to look out of the window.

'If I'm telling stories, you can whack me with your slipper.'

So Grandfather looked out of the window.

Joey held his breath. Was the Orange Tree still there? He closed his eyes.

'Suffering Catfish!' whispered Grandfather. (He always said that when he was surprised.)

Joey and Grandfather stood in silence for a long time gazing at the Orange Tree. At last Grandfather said, 'Well, I guess we'd better tell your Pa.'

'He'll never believe you,' said Joey. 'I've tried.'

'He'll believe me,' said Grandfather firmly.

Joey's mother and father were still lying in bed with the bedclothes pulled over their ears when Joey and his grandfather entered the room. Grandfather nudged Joey to speak first.

'Ma! Pa! I wish to inform you that there is an Orange Tree in our backyard.'

The two humps under the bedclothes didn't stir.

'Did you hear what Joey said?' bellowed Grandfather – with such a roar that Joey's Ma and Pa sat bolt upright like jack-in-the-boxes.

'There is an Orange Tree in the backyard.'

Ma and Pa got out of bed and went to the window.

'*Suffering Catfish!*' they gasped with astonishment. 'There is an Orange Tree.'

'What do we do now, Grandfather?' asked Joey.

'What do we do? Why, we pick as many oranges as we can and then ask all our neighbours in for a party!'

So they all got dressed and rushed out into the backyard with poles and baskets and a ladder and began to pick the oranges.

Soon they had several baskets full. Then Joey's ma put on her best Sunday hat and went round to all the neighbours inviting them to a party.

Everyone agreed that it was the best party in years. The boys got out their guitars and drums, and everyone danced and sang long into the evening. As for the oranges, they got eaten up with the speed of lightning.

'Oh my, I haven't tasted oranges like this since I was a boy,' said Grandfather dreamily, sucking his fifth orange.

'It's just like home,' said one old lady.

'Where did you get them?' asked another.

'We got a tree,' said Ma.

'Ha ha ha ha ha ...' the guests roared with laughter.

'My, oh my, an orange tree did you say...in your backyard? Ha ha ha ha.'

Soon the whole party was rocking with laughter. Ma ran to the window and pulled back the curtain. 'See for yourselves,' she said.

Outside it was night. The sky was starry and bright with a new moon. The backyard was empty. The Orange Tree had gone. Everyone ran outside.

'Look!' cried Joey, collecting some sprigs of fallen leaves.

'This proves the tree was here.'

Everyone stopped laughing. They looked at the leaves and sniffed the air which was rich with the smell of oranges. Somehow they all knew that it was true. Amazed, they thanked Joey, his ma, pa and his grandfather for the party, and went home to talk about the miraculous Orange Tree.

Joey pressed the orange leaves in a book. Whenever it was a dull, grey, rainy day, he would open the book and a faint smell of oranges would float upwards and remind him of that summer, when for one day an Orange Tree had stood in his own backyard.

Jamila Gavin

A moving story

I was only half listening to dad that morning. I heard him say that he'd pick me up after school but I stopped paying attention after that. Afterwards I wished I had listened. At least I'd have been prepared for the shock I got later. Dad sat in the car at the end of the school drive. Mum was there and Susie my little sister. The whole family, except for Sooty. He would be at home curled up in his favourite armchair.

So where were we going? It wasn't anybody's birthday as far as I remembered so it couldn't be the burger bar. Or the supermarket. Not the whole family. I suddenly panicked. It must be the dentist's. Time for a check up, or a polish, or a filling or three.

We were driving into town. It must be the dentist's. I thought, until dad carried on past the turn. 'Not far now,' mum said, looking over her shoulder.

We stopped in one of the narrow streets in the old part of town. Opposite a factory. Perhaps we were visiting, but I didn't know anyone who lived there.

'Here we are,' Dad said. 'Out you get you two.'

My curiosity finally got the better of me.

'Where?' I asked.

'Our new house,' he replied pointing to a sold sign fixed to the wall. 'I told you this morning.'

He told me this morning. And I hadn't listened. I couldn't believe it. It was a bombshell.

'New house? Why do we want a new house?'

Now no-one was listening to me. Dad had opened the door and they'd gone inside.

I never got any answers later on either. Everyone ignored me.

'Why are we moving?'

'I don't want to go.'

'I like it where we are.'

No-one listened.

Inside everywhere was so dark. The wallpaper was brown with dark green patterns, and was peeling off at the corners. There were no carpets or curtains or furniture. And it was so cold. No radiators, just open fireplaces with blackened walls. I looked out of the kitchen window. There was a wall around the overgrown garden. Mum and Susie were poking around in the long grass. I could hear dad banging about in the front room. They'd all forgotten about me. So I went upstairs to the bathroom, locked the door, sat on the toilet, and sulked.

I thought about all the homes I knew. That I'd been inside. Ours of course, my friend's Jamie's , Uncle Pete's and finally gran's. Gran's was my favourite, all cosy and cluttered. Full of oversize furniture, pictures and potted plants. And then I remembered her story. The one she always told about when mum was a little girl. I could hear her talking.

'We were moving to a new house and your mum didn't want to go. It was miles away from her school and friends. The day we moved she cried all the way in the furniture van. If it hadn't been for Whiskers I think she'd have jumped out and run all the way back to the old house. But she was too busy clutching the cat in her arms. She daren't let it go. Almost as if she knew what was about to happen. We'd only been in the house a few minutes when the cat went missing. We looked everywhere. Bedrooms, cupboards, the garden, even the attic. Grandad and your mum searched all the streets and gardens round about. We even went all the way back to our old house the next day to see if it had made its way there. But no luck.

Whiskers had gone.

We were well and truly moved in by now. Furniture, curtains, rugs, bedding, crockery, pots and pans, clothes. But without the cat the house still seemed empty. One afternoon we were sitting in the living room after dinner when there was a scratching noise from the chimney. Lumps of soot began to drop into the empty grate. At first we thought it was a bird, but then your mum rushed across to the fireplace and reached up inside. Moments later she was holding Whiskers as tightly as in the furniture van. Fancy the cat hiding up the chimney for two whole days. So we changed her name. Whiskers didn't suit her anymore. She was Sooty from that day on.'

Gran's story. My favourite house and at first no-one wanted to live there, not even a cat.

Suddenly I knew that we could be happy in this house too. Mum, Dad, Susie, me and OUR Sooty. Named after gran's cat. I got off the toilet seat and unlocked the door. But it wouldn't budge. No matter how hard I tugged it wouldn't move. It was stuck. I banged and shouted until I heard dad run up the stairs. He stopped outside the door. 'Well, well Simon,' he said. 'It looks as if you'll have to stay here now whether you like it or not.'

Liz Lawman

The King's elephant

In the dead of night, a gang of thieves crept into the King of Benares' elephant-house to plot their next job. Their leader had already carried out more than a hundred violent crimes. Now he described to his friends his plan for breaking into the royal treasury to steal all the King's jewels.

'What happens if someone comes along while we're doing the job?' asked the youngest thief.

'In our line of work you've got to be prepared to kill anyone who gets in your way,' the leader replied coldly.

Now, the King's favourite elephant heard all this and thought that the criminals had come there to teach him the right way to behave. So, next morning when his keeper came to feed him, he picked the poor man up in his mighty trunk and threw him on the floor. And he attacked anyone else who tried to get near him. Eventually, the other keepers had to toss ropes around him and tie him up to stop him doing any more mischief.

When the King was told about this, he was very upset. He was very fond of the elephant, which up to that time had always been well behaved.

'It really would break my heart to have to put him down,' he told his ministers, shaking his head. 'I can't understand what's got into him.'

The King then sent his wisest minister to the elephant-house to see whether he could find out anything. The minister looked around carefully and, in the straw that was scattered on the floor, he found some things that the thieves had left behind.

'Aha!' he exclaimed. 'Very useful clues!' And he hurried back to the palace.

'What seems to have happened, Your Majesty,' he told the King, 'is that the elephant was led astray by listening to criminals who were meeting in the elephant-house.'

'What can we do then to set matters right?' the King asked.

'I suggest we put good men in the elephant's stall and have them sing the praises of gentleness, patience, kindness and generosity,' the minister replied. 'That may lead him back into decent ways.'

'Let it be done then,' commanded the King.

So a group of honest men sat in the elephant's stall talking about good things for several weeks. The elephant pinned back his great ears and listened carefully. He now took his lesson from what they had to say — and for the rest of his life he was the nicest, kindest, most gentle animal you could hope to meet anywhere.

John Snelling

Growing up

Once upon a time, as all good stories begin, there was a boy named Barnaby. Barnaby's parents were quite well off and they had a large garden. The garden had a tall thick hedge all round it so that Barnaby could play safely there. But as Barnaby grew older he grew curious. Curious to know what was on the other side of the hedge.

He searched and searched until he found a small hole in the hedge. Through it he saw there was on the other side a great big world with traffic and people and movement and large impressive buildings. Then Barnaby's curiosity grew even stronger. He became determined to go through the hedge to explore the big exciting world that he had glimpsed.

So one day he got together his favourite things – his Teddy bear, his toy train and his box of bricks and tucking them under his arms he tried to get through the hole in the hedge. But though he struggled and pushed he found he could not get through. 'Oh blow!' he said to himself. He was very annoyed, but he did not give up.

The next day Barnaby decided he would try again. 'If I leave the box of bricks behind then I might be able to get through' he thought. So with his Teddy and his toy train under his arms he tried again. But though he pushed and wriggled and squirmed with all his might he just could not get through. Barnaby was very disappointed, but still determined.

So the next day he thought, 'If I leave the toy train behind then surely I will get through'. So with just his favourite Teddy under his arm he tried again. Yet no matter how hard he twisted and shoved and heaved he just could not get through.

Barnaby was puffed and quite cross about it. But he did not give up. He was determined to have another try the next day.

Then Barnaby had to make a very difficult decision. He would have to leave his Teddy behind. Barnaby was terribly sad about it because his Teddy was his favourite and had been his companion for as long as he could remember. But there was no way he was going to get through that hole in the hedge otherwise.

So Barnaby sadly said goodbye to his Teddy and all alone Barnaby tried again. And though it was not easy, and he had to push and squeeze very hard, at last Barnaby got through the hole in the hedge. There he was in the great big exciting world he had only glimpsed before!

Barnaby's story is a story about growing up: that growing up is not without difficulties and is sometimes painful and that sacrifices have to be made, just as Barnaby had to leave his Teddy behind.

St. Paul told us about it in the Gospels when he wrote:

'When I was a child, I spake as a child, I understood as a child, I thought as child, but when I became a man I put away childish things.'

John Cotton

Prince Siddhartha

There was once an Indian prince named Siddhartha. His family wished to keep him away from all pain, ugliness and unpleasantness. So he was not allowed outside the palace grounds and only the most beautiful and handsome people were employed to attend him. They made sure that he saw only the most perfect flowers, ate only the very best food and nothing that was broken or spoilt should be allowed near him. But once a year the young Prince had to take part in a religious procession through the city to the Temple for a special ceremony.

In spite of all precautions, the old and the sick being forbidden to be anywhere along the route of the procession, Prince Siddhartha caught sight of a sick man in the crowd that lined the road to the Temple. This worried the Prince as he had not seen a sick person before. He asked about it, what was it? but was told that he should not concern himself about such things.

The next year the precautions were doubled. Nevertheless a very old woman managed to be in the crowd watching the procession as it passed. Prince Siddhartha saw her. She was very wrinkled and bent and her arms were like withered twigs. This worried the Prince deeply. He asked about her but was not given very straightforward answers.

The third year he was to see something that worried him even more. It was a dead man lying in the road along which the procession passed. He had collapsed and died as he waited for the procession to come by. Once again the Prince asked questions but they were brushed aside. Nevertheless the Prince could not stop thinking and worrying about what he had seen.

These thoughts led him to the conclusion that there was much he had to learn about the world outside the palace grounds. So he decided to abandon his riches, his beautiful young wife and the luxurious life of the palace. With the help of a trusted servant he slipped out of the palace at night when everyone else was asleep.

When he had ridden a long way from the palace he changed his rich clothes with those of his servant, and gave the servant his jewels and his horse and said goodbye.

At first Siddhartha decided he would find the truth of things by giving up all luxuries and pleasures. In time he had given up everything and was living in the forest on just one grain of rice a day. Not surprisingly it was not long before he collapsed from weakness and starvation.

Fortunately he was found by a woodcutter's daughter who was walking in the forest. She took him home, nursed him and fed him and Prince Siddhartha recovered. And he had learnt an important lesson. That was the lesson of the Middle Way. The way between the extreme luxury of his early life and the extreme poverty of his life in the forest. And this Middle Way led Siddhartha to other great truths about how we should conduct our lives and behave towards others.

Thus he obtained enlightenment and became a Buddha. Others came to learn from him. Today, two and a half thousand years later, Buddha has millions of followers all over the world practising the Middle Way of Buddhism. They also strive to become Buddhas themselves by gaining merit from doing good works and caring for others.

We could learn from the story of Prince Siddhartha too.

John Cotton

That Christmassy feeling

School had finished for the holidays. As I walked the last few hundred yards home I felt all Christmassy and happy.

Outside my house I stood still and looked around. Everywhere was strangely quiet. The clear sky was dotted with hundreds of sparkling stars and it was bitterly cold. Roofs were white with frost. The whole street and houses and hedges and trees were just like scenery on a Christmas card. Any minute now I knew I must step out of the picture and into the real world.

I reached out and brushed the stiff icy leaves of the hedge in our front garden. The cat moving suddenly from its shelter under the bush was real enough. It shook the frost from its coat and scurried across the lawn before squeezing under the fence and disappearing.

I told my mum when I got inside.

'I saw it this morning,' she said. 'It looked like a stray to me. Ran like a scared rabbit when I opened the back door.'

Mum looked across the kitchen table. She knew what I was thinking.

'Forget it Steven. It's old, it's a stray and it's having kittens soon. We can't possibly take it in.'

Dad agreed.

'And it's too soon after Whiskers,' he said sadly.

I'd lost that Christmassy feeling. Cards and a tissue paper stained-glass window lay untouched in my school bag. I'd looked out of the front window several times during the evening searching for the cat. There was nothing magical about the street anymore. Clouds had swallowed up the stars and it had begun to rain.

When dad climbed the stepladder into the loft to search for the box of decorations and tree lights I wasn't interested.

'Come on Steven,' he said. 'Cheer up. It's nearly Christmas.'

I saw the cat every day. It became a regular visitor. Mum put a bowl of food out on the back lawn each afternoon and I watched it feed from the kitchen window. I daren't go any closer, it was still very nervous.

'I don't like encouraging her,' mum said, 'but I can't see her starve. Especially in her condition.'

I began to hope she might change her mind. And then change dad's. I knew what he'd meant. Nobody missed Whiskers more than me. He was a present on the day I started school. A fluffy black kitten. Then there was the accident and I was only just getting used to coming home and him not being there. But there was still a dent in the cushion in the chair next to the fire where he always slept and scratch marks on the stair carpet where he sharpened his claws.

Hope became wishes.

But the card in the newsagent's window soon put paid to my dreams. I saw it when I went to pay for the papers on the day before Christmas Eve.

'Lost. Tabby cat. Treasured family pet. Please contact Mr J Eales, 27 Milldale Road. Tel 20739.'

I didn't know what to do. Part of me wanted to ignore it. Pretend I hadn't seen it. Then perhaps we could adopt the cat. But I couldn't keep it to myself. What if Whiskers had strayed? How would I have felt then?

Dad rang that evening. Milldale Road was only a few streets away. Apparently they'd only just moved house and the cat had wandered off. Mr Eales arranged to come round the next afternoon when it came out of hiding to feed.

The first flakes of snow began to fall during the morning. By the middle of the afternoon it had settled quite thickly on the lawn. We had all gathered in the kitchen to watch and wait. Mr Eales was all ready to rush out and grab the cat as soon as it appeared. But she was late. The food bowl began to fill up with snow. I half hoped she wouldn't come and there was a chance we could keep her. But then I began to worry that something nasty had happened. Perhaps she had run into the road like Whiskers. Whiskers who knew the busy street far better than she.

It was beginning to get dark. Mr Eales was ready to leave and try again the next day – Christmas Day, until my mum said.

'How about a cup of tea before you go?'

Everyone trooped into the living room and sat round the fire. It needed making up.

'Steven, fetch some wood there's a good lad,' dad said.

I trudged down the path to the shed. Snow was heaped around the door and I had to force it open. Light from the kitchen window flooded into the darkened building. The cat was lying on a sack on top of the wood pile. Everywhere was quiet except for the rasping sound of a rough tongue.

And there she was, licking her kittens, two of them, one tabby, like her mother and the other black.

Nervously I drew the door back and returned to the house. As I walked into the living room the Christmassy feeling came back. Until then I'd hardly noticed how bright and cheerful the room looked. Decorations hung from the ceiling and walls. Coloured lights shone from the tree in the corner. I thought about those kittens snuggling up in the shed and smiled. I had a feeling that my secret Christmas wish was coming true after all.

Ian Addis

Hazel

The tree stood at the bottom of next door's garden. It wasn't a tall tree as trees grow. But in Summer it was home to dozens of birds that flocked among its branches for food and shelter. Blackbirds, thrushes, finches, pigeons, sparrows. Even the occasional woodpecker.

In winter old Mrs Jacobs would hang coconut halves and pieces of fat to attract the blue tits.

It wasn't a beautiful tree as trees grow, but in Spring yellow, powdery catkins hung over the wall and in Autumn plump, ripe nuts dropped into the flower beds below.

But it was a special tree to me.

Dad told me its name. Hazel. Just like mine.

Mrs Jacobs was a widow. When the weather was fine she pottered around outside weeding the borders and keeping everywhere tidy. If it was cold or wet she stayed indoors playing patience or doing huge jigsaws with hundreds of pieces on the kitchen table under the window. Sometimes if the weather was really bad we did her shopping at the supermarket and when I took it round she always gave me toffees from the tin on the shelf above the mantelpiece. She still had coal fires. My dad tried to persuade her to change to gas or electric but she was stubborn.

'I like to see a flame,' she always said. 'There's company in a real fire.'

Dad kept her in sticks. But it was my job on Sundays to make sure her coal bucket was filled for the week from the heap in the shed down the garden.

As winter set in I saw less and less of the old lady.

Sometimes frost stayed all day on the path outside her back door and she didn't go out at all.

Its funny how you seem to know something's going to happen long before it does. It might be good. Like you set off for school on the morning of a netball match and you know you're going to play well. Somehow you can sense it. You can catch, you can throw, you can aim.

Then there's the other sort of day.

From the minute you wake up, the clock's slow. You drop the toast butter side down, you run out of toothpaste. Your mum nags you to hurry up, you answer back, she raises her voice, you slam the door .....

A bad day.

And you've forgotten your swimming kit.

Mr Sutton asks 'Is anyone at home at lunchtimes?'

You say 'No but I've got a back door key.'

'Go and fetch it,' he says, 'but be careful crossing the road.'

That's what happened that Monday.

I knew something was wrong by the kitchen chimney. No smoke.

I scrambled up the wall and saw old Mrs Jacobs lying all crumpled outside the back door and I guessed what had happened.

I'd forgotten to fill the bucket with coal. It lay next to her on the icy path where it had fallen. It was all my fault.

The ambulance was there in minutes. They wrapped her up in thick blankets and lifted her into the back on a stretcher.

When she came out of hospital she never returned to the house.

Dad said she'd moved away to live with her daughter. So the house was put up for sale. There was a big board nailed to the wall outside in the street.

Mum asked if dad thought it would sell quickly.

'Needs a lot doing to it. Central heating, double glazing, new kitchen ....'

But someone did buy it. After a couple of weeks the sign had a sold sticker on, and later I heard some people talking in the garden.

Guess what they said.

'The first thing we'll do is cut down that ugly tree. It's too big for the garden.'

I didn't wait to hear anymore. I rushed inside, haunted by the words. Cut down that tree. That ugly tree. My special tree. That was to be my punishment.

For weeks the new people were backwards and forwards decorating the house from top to bottom. But they hadn't touched the tree yet.

'They will when they've finished inside,' dad said knowingly.

'By the way,' mum said. 'They're called Cooper and they've got children. A boy and a girl. I think. That'll brighten the place up.'

I didn't see anyone again until the day the family moved in. We went round to help unload the van. When we'd finished everyone sat in the kitchen drinking tea.

Mrs Cooper was staring out at the garden for several minutes.

'Colin,' she said at last. 'Look at your ugly tree.'

Mr Cooper joined her at the window. I wondered what she'd seen, but when I looked I soon realised.

Catkins were beginning to form on the branches. Pale yellow ribbons fluttering in the breeze. The first signs of spring after the long winter.

'It's a hazel,' I said quietly.

'Well we couldn't chop that down then could we Colin?'

Mrs Cooper chuckled. And they both laughed.

So did their little girl.

'I'm called Hazel too,' she said.

Liz Lawman

Buried treasure

Have you ever dreamed of being rich? You'd be a very unusual person if you haven't. Even King Midas with all his wealth wished for a golden touch. Medieval alchemists spent their lives vainly attempting to turn base metal to gold. Prospectors trekked hundreds of miles to the North American goldfields in search of the few precious nuggets that would make their fortune. And my dad did the football pools every week for sixty years without winning the price of a first class stamp.

But Eric Lawes did it. Eric who?

Don't worry, I hadn't heard of him either until recently.

How did he do it then?

When he retired as a gardener a few years ago Eric needed a hobby. Not just any hobby, but one which would take him out into the Suffolk countryside around his home. So he bought a metal detector. You've seen people with them I'm sure. At the seaside, hordes endlessly scouring the beach to unearth a handful of bottle tops and the odd useless backdoor key.

Eric was different.

'I like the solitude of just going off on my own in a field to see what I can discover,' he explained. The most he expected to find on that fateful Autumn morning was lost tools belonging to a farmer friend.

'Keep a sharp look out for my hammer,' Farmer Whatling shouted as Eric trudged watchfully across the freshly ploughed field. Experienced eyes scanned the surface. Ears listened for the warning bleep from the detector.

There it was. Urgent. Insistent. He knelt down, sifted the soft soil through his fingers, and found his fortune. As he said later,

'It's impossible to describe my feelings when I found one silver coin, then a second, then went down a bit further and struck gold. I decided to stop when I had filled two plastic carrier bags and put them in the car, because there must have been about a hundredweight of coins and treasure still in the ground.'

He'd unearthed the contents of an iron bound oak chest buried 1600 years ago by a wealthy Roman family. Solid gold bracelets, figurines, necklaces, spoons, pendants encrusted with precious jewels, containers and thousands of gold and silver coins. A hoard worth several million pounds.

What to do next? Well there were several things he could have done. But Eric Lawes was as sensible as he was honest. He understood the importance of his find and alerted Farmer Whatling. He immediately telephoned the landowners, Suffolk County Council. Both men were sworn to secrecy. Imagine how Eric must have felt when he arrived home for lunch with a car boot full of treasure, but couldn't tell his wife. Police were posted at the farm to guard the field while archaeologists carefully removed the remaining items from the ground. These were stored in the local police station overnight before being transported the following day to the British Museum for cleaning and cataloguing. Experts were quick to praise Eric.

'It is unique for a major hoard of this kind to be properly excavated, and full credit must to go Mr Lawes for reporting it so promptly.

The finder remained remarkably unimpressed by his success.

'It's everybody's dream when they use a metal detector to find treasure,' he said. 'but the beauty of it is I wasn't even looking for valuables – only farm tools. And I found the hammer as well.'

It is extremely unlikely that the original owners will return to claim their property. In all probability it will be declared treasure trove and become the property of the Crown. This will guarantee Mr Lawes a sizeable share of its value almost certainly making him a millionaire.

Asked what he will do with his fortune he replied, 'My wife is disabled, so I will probably buy a bungalow and perhaps a new car.'

And are his treasure seeking days over?

He answered with a chuckle.

'I look forward to heading into the open countryside with my metal detector and making another great discovery one day.'

With his luck, he'd better make sure his new car has an extra large boot!

Tom Quincey

Marzipanned

We loaded the supermarket trolley. Eggs, butter, sugar, flour, spice, almonds, dried fruit. All the ingredients for the special Easter Cake. A Simnel cake mum called it.

That afternoon my sister Jackie and me helped mum to weigh everything and stir it all up in a big bowl. Then she poured half the mixture into a cake tin.

'Ready now for the marzipan,' she said.

We watched as she mixed the ground almonds and sugar with egg yolk and essence.

We loved marzipan.

Then she rolled out part of the rich, golden paste and spread it over the cake in the tin, before pouring the rest of the mixture on top. Then she put it in the oven. We looked hopefully at the yellow mound lying on the work top, but mum shook her head.

'That's for later,' she said, reading our minds.

'You can scrape out the bowl if you like.'

So we had to be satisfied with that.

When the cake was cooked mum waited until it was cold before brushing apricot jam over the top and covering it with another round of marzipan.

But there was still some left over. Once again our eyes lit up.

'It's not for you,' she said. 'You're out of luck. It's for the disciples.'

And with that she began rolling the rest into little balls and placing them around the edge of the cake. We'd lost interest by then.

She put the cake in a tin and left it high on a shelf in the pantry. Until Easter Sunday.

Jackie and I both knew it was there. One morning when we went to get crisps for our school lunches I caught her stealing a quick glance up at the shelf. I knew what she was thinking. I'd got the same idea. Those small round marzipan disciples.

Suddenly a terrible thought came to me. What if she'd already helped herself? It worried me all day at school. I couldn't ask her. So I waited until we were both in the pantry again. Then I stared up at the cake tin and waited.

It didn't take long.

'Shall we?' she whispered.

'Just one,' I answered.

'Each,' she said.

My sister's just a bit taller than me. Stretching up, she prised the lid off with her thumbs and reached inside. So expertly. She must have done it before. In seconds the lid was pressed back

into place and two balls of marzipan sat invitingly in her outstretched palm. But not for long. My mouth soon relished that wonderful almond taste. I wanted it to last forever. Jackie was turning the marzipan round and round with her tongue, draining every drop of flavour.

At last we closed the pantry door behind us as if nothing had happened. It was that easy.

I knew the day of reckoning would come. When the cake was put on the tea table on Easter Sunday with half the disciples missing there would be music to be faced. But at least I needn't face it on my own. And Jackie had thought of it first.

So I went back to the tin. That mouthwatering taste drew me like a magnet. Again and again. Until one day when I went to the pantry there were none left.

And then I began to panic.

Once, well, was understandable, forgivable even. But between us we'd taken them all. The lot.

I told Jackie but she already knew.

'What shall we do?' I asked. She was my big sister. She'd know. And anyway it was her fault wasn't it?

'Make some more,' she said.

Of course! Why hadn't I thought of that? We'd watched mum make them hadn't we?

'We'll go to the supermarket on Saturday morning and buy the ingredients, with our pocket money,' Jackie said, all matter of fact.

So we did. Then we hurried home before mum got back from town, got out the mixing bowl and made the marzipan decorations. The disciples.

They looked perfect, arranged around the edge of the cake. Exactly like before.

On Easter Sunday we helped mum set the table. Knives and forks for the salad, cups and saucers, and little plates for the cake. The Simnel cake. Mum brought in the tin from the pantry and lifted the cake out ready to set it on the stand in the middle of the table cloth.

But she didn't put it down.

She was staring at the cake.

'Is something wrong mum?' Jackie asked.

'It certainly is,' she replied, her eyes flashing dangerously. She pointed to the shapes arranged in a ring on top.

She knew. I didn't know how, but she knew.

'Twelve,' I confidently explained. 'One for each disciple.'

'But there should only be eleven,' she said, removing one of the balls. 'There's no place for Judas Iscariot.'

'I wonder how he got there?'

Ian Addis

Fair exchange is no robbery

It was such a hot afternoon. Peter rushed through the front door into the hall on his way to the fridge and that bottle of ice cold lemonade. It had filled his thoughts on the way home from school. 'Is that you Peter?' His mother's voice echoed from the living room. 'Come and see what I've got for you.' The drink was forgotten. What could his present be? It sat waiting for him, on the table in front of the window. Peter picked it up and held it tenderly. Slowly turning it round in his hands he was careful not to bruise the smooth, shiny skin. It was the biggest, reddest apple he had ever seen.

'I got it from the market especially for you,' his mother said.

'I know you like apples.'

Just as he was about to bite into the crisp, sweet flesh he glanced out of the window.

In the garden next door Katie Pope was gently swaying to and fro on her swing. She was clutching something in her lap.

'Peter be a love and pop to the post-box with this letter please,' his mother said over his shoulder.

'OK mum,' he replied. Of course he'd do that. He couldn't wait. Dropping the apple on to the table he grabbed the envelope, raced out the front door and round to Katie's house. She was still swinging backwards and forwards. And she was still holding the largest, roundest orange he had ever seen.

'Hello Peter,' she said. 'What do you want?'

He came straight to the point.

'Your orange,' he said. 'But I'll give you my apple in exchange.'

'Alright,' she replied. Just like that. She didn't argue. She just handed him the monster fruit.

'Where's the apple then?'

'I'm just going to the post-box. When I come back I'll fetch you the apple. Promise.'

'Good,' she said. 'I don't like oranges anyway.'

Carrying the envelope in one hand and the orange in the other he hurried down the street. Alan Carter was crossing the road towards him holding huge ice-cream cornet with a chocolate flake sticking out the top.

Peter remembered how hot and thirsty he was.

'Hello Alan,' he shouted. 'Fancy a swap? This juicy orange for your ice-cream?'

Alright,' he replied, just like that. Just like Katie. Peter was surprised but handed over the orange and took the cornet.

'It's too hot for ice-cream,' Alan observed wisely.

'There'll be hardly any left unless you eat it quickly. But this orange will last for hours.'

Seconds later Peter was wondering if he had made the right choice. Little rivers of ice-cream were already beginning to trickle down between his fingers.

Then he saw Becky Miller pushing her bike out of a gateway near the post-box. She was holding a packet of salt and vinegar crisps. His favourite flavour.

'Have I missed the ice-cream van Peter?' she asked anxiously.

'Yes but never mind, you can have mine,' he replied craftily, ' for your crisps.'

'That's kind,' Becky replied taking the cornet.

'Sometimes really you're nice Peter.'

And she gave him the bag of crisps.

He quickly slipped the letter into the post-box and hurried back home.

He passed Becky Miller straddling her bicycle and licking the ice-cream.

He passed Alan Carter sitting on a wall peeling the orange.

He passed Katie Pope still swaying on her garden swing and remembered his promise.

The thought of the big red apple on the table by the window and his mouth began to water.

'Would you rather have a packet of crisps?' he shouted as he went down his front path, crossing his fingers for good luck.

'Only if they're salt and vinegar,' she answered.

'Oh they are,' he replied gratefully. 'They are.'

For the first time she jumped down from the swing and ran across to the fence between the two gardens. Then she reached across for the crisps.

'Thanks,' she said sweetly. 'Sometimes you're really nice Peter.'

But the compliment was wasted. Peter couldn't wait to dash through the front door and into the house.

His dad was in the kitchen emptying the bottle of lemonade into a glass.

Peter pushed past him into the living room.

There was no big red apple on the table in front of the window.

But in the wastepaper basket, perched on top of a mound of crumpled newspapers and used tissues, sat a huge, great core.

His father's voice echoed from the other room.

'Thanks for leaving me the present,' he said.

'It was the sweetest apple I've ever tasted.'

Liz Lawman

Crab's Kingdom

In the beginning there was a rock pool.

It was older than human memory. Year after year the sea had worn away at the rocks until the pool was a smooth hollow. When the tide came in, the pool became shadowy and mysterious. When the tide went out it became a shining basin of clear water. It never overflowed and never became dry.

The pool was a kingdom of its own. If you looked into its depths you could see many living things: fish and starfish, silent limpets and lively hermit crabs, shrimps and sea anemones. And sometimes, if you watched carefully, you could see a creature with a fine shell of mottled brown and white.

That was Crab, the king of the rock pool.

Like most kings, Crab had a rather good life.

He had long legs and sharp pincers. He could run faster than any other creature in the pool. He was the strongest animal in his kingdom, and he could not help being rather proud.

He lived in a dark hole under a ledge of rock. Near his stronghold the pool was shallow and its floor was flat and sandy. But at the other end, where the water was deeper, a forest of feathery weeds grew right up to the gateway which led into the open sea.

Sometimes, when the weather was stormy, the tide would wash some strange creature into the pool, but usually life in the pool was peaceful. Tides rose and fell, bringing in food and fresh water. The sun shone by day. At night the pool gleamed under the dark sky.

At least, that was how things were until the day when the invasion began...

It began like any other day. The first specks of sunlight touched the pool. The Crab went out of his stronghold and felt the swirl of water around him. The tide was coming in. It was time to go hunting.

The Crab set off towards the forest. On his way he greeted the quiet contented limpets and the hermit crabs which scuttled about in their funny top-heavy shells.

The Crab took a narrow path which led to the depths of the forest. The tall weeds waved close around him. The sunlight disappeared.

Suddenly the Crab stopped.

In the darkness ahead he could see something strange. It lay near the entrance to the pool. Perhaps it was some unknown enemy from the sea beyond? The Crab gathered his courage and sidled towards the stranger.

It was not like anything he had ever seen before. It was long and shining, almost like a fish, but it was not a fish. It didn't seem to be alive. It drifted on the surface of the pool. It gleamed coldly in the sunlight.

The Thing remained there all day. By the next morning it had

sunk to the bottom of the pool. Little by little the creatures in the pool became used to the strange Thing. Soon the hermit crabs were playing around it without fear.

But before long, two more strange Things had appeared in the little kingdom. One was like the first invader. The other was quite different. It was soft and waving, like weed, but it had no colour. It floated round the pool, and at last became stuck in a crack of rock, almost blocking the entrance to Crab's stronghold.

As time went on, more and more strange Things arrived. Some were large and some were small, some hard and some soft. They were all different shapes and colours. Not one of them was alive, but unlike dead things they did not fade and disappear.

The beautiful pool became dirty and crowded.

One day, the Crab climbed out of his pool to lie in the sun. He had just stretched himself out on a dry sandy rock when he noticed a strange sight. A line of hermit crabs was coming out of the pool. When they saw him, they tried to hide.

'Where are you going to?' asked the King Crab.

The hermit crabs shuffled about uncomfortably.

'Well, you see, Your Majesty,' said one of them, 'we've decided to leave the pool. It used to be a nice clean place, but ever since those strange Things started to appear, the water's been getting dirtier and dirtier. We can't live here any more. We're going to find another pool ...'

The King Crab was silent. There was nothing he could say. He looked down at his pool. Sure enough, its waters were becoming grey and dirty.

'Go,' he said softly. 'Go, and I wish you good luck. But I will stay in my pool. Good-bye.'

For a long time he stared down at his kingdom, spread out below the smooth, sunny rocks. When he looked round, the hermit crabs had gone. Slowly, Crab crept back into his pool.

The next morning, when Crab left his stronghold, he realised at once that something was seriously wrong.

The tide had stopped. The water was not flowing in from the sea. All was as still as death. Not a ripple stirred in the pool.

Then the Crab saw what had happened. A cluster of strange Things had become wedged among the rocks. They were completely blocking the narrow gateway which joined the pool to the sea beyond.

The Crab was horrified. The tide from the sea was the life-blood of the pool. Without it, how could he find food? How could the water in the pool stay fresh? Already he could feel the murky stillness poisoning his body. He ran to the gateway and tore at the Things with his strong claws, but his grasp slipped on their slimy surface. The Things remained as firmly stuck as ever.

They have won, thought the Crab. They have killed my world. But I have only one kingdom. I cannot leave it. I will stay here until I die.

But if only, he sighed, if only someone could rescue my kingdom...

That same morning a boy came to the seashore. He walked barefoot over the rocks.

Now and then he stopped to pick up twisted shells or smooth pebbles. Best of all, he liked to gaze into rock pools. At first he could see nothing in them but sea water and weeds. But then he saw that they were full of life. He saw the darting specks of fishes. He watched anemones slowly changing from blobs of jelly into delicate flowers. It was like discovering a new world.

But the boy found one pool which was not full of life. It was close to a beach which had become covered with rubbish. Picnickers had left empty cans and bottles on the sand. The tide had washed up plastic bags and broken toys.

The waters of this pool were grey and dirty. Nothing seemed to move in them except for evil bubbles which rose to the surface with a plop.

It was Crab's kingdom.

The boy felt sad when he saw the pool. He decided to clean it.

First, with a sharp stick, he fished out all the rubbish which floated on the pool. He cleared its blocked entrance, and he collected all the other litter which was scattered over the rocks and sand.

Then the boy began to dig a pit in the sand. The sun grew hot overhead, but still the boy dug. By noon he had made a deep, dark hole in the beach. He pushed all the rubbish into the hole and covered it with a thick layer of sand.

Next he found some pieces of wood and made large signs. The signs read:

PLEASE DO NOT THROW
YOUR RUBBISH HERE.

He put two signs on the beach and one on the rocks. Then he went home. Darkness gathered above the sea. The inky waves broke over the empty, clean sand and the shining rocks.

The boy went back every day to look at the pool. The tide had begun to flow again. The sea washed away the stagnant water and the dead weeds. But still there seemed to be no life in the pool.

Then on the third day the boy saw something moving. Slowly, a creature appeared from under a ledge of rock. It was a crab. It had a mottled brown and white shell. It moved slowly, as if it was dazed, but even so the boy could see that this was the king of the pool.

To the Crab, it seemed as if it had all been a dream.

The strange Things which had almost killed his kingdom went as they had come, into the unknown.

The tide flowed. Light shone through water. Plants grew again. Slowly, the other creatures returned: the fish, the starfish, the anemones, and last of all the hermit crabs, timidly scuttling back to their old home. In a small corner of the wide sea life began again, almost as if nothing had happened.

Tessa Morris-Suzuki

The doko

In a small village in Nepal lived a man and his wife and their small boy. They were very poor and often they didn't have enough to eat. Moreover, the man's father lived with them. He had worked hard all his life, but now he was too old to work any more and he had no one else to look after him.

The old man needed a lot of looking after. His son and his daughter-in-law grumbled at him and neglected him, so the old man was thin and dirty. His clothes were worn out and he shivered all night on his mat in the corner where he tried to sleep. Most of the time he had only scraps of leftover food to eat. Sometimes the boy shared his food with his grandfather, but once his mother saw him.

'What do you think you're doing?' she asked sharply.

'Grandfather's hungry,' the boy answered.

'You leave grandfather alone,' said his mother. 'We've enough trouble as it is. And don't let me see you wasting good food again.'

The boy talked to his grandfather and helped him when he could do so without being found out, but things got worse. The old man coughed and complained. His son and daughter-in-law became more and more short-tempered with him. They had nothing to spare for him and he was in the way.

One night when he should have been asleep the boy heard his parents whispering together.

'It would have to be a long way away,' he heard his mother say. 'So far away he couldn't come back.'

'Perhaps someone will feel sorry for him,' his father said. 'If I leave him by the side of the road someone might take him in and feed him.'

'They *might*,' said his mother, 'but one thing is certain. We can't put up with him any longer. After all, we've got the boy to think of.'

'I'll need something to carry him in. I'd better go to market tomorrow and get a good, strong doko.'

'Yes,' his wife said, 'and you can take him tomorrow night when there is no one about. We'll tell the neighbours that he wanted to spend his last days in peace and he's gone to live in a holy place.'

When the boy woke in the morning his father had already left for market.

'What are you going to do to grandfather?' he asked.

His mother was startled.

'Nothing,' she said. 'Why?'

'Yes you are,' said the boy. 'I know you are. You're going to throw him away.'

'That will do!' said his mother angrily.

'Whatever put an idea like that in your head? No. No, you see grandfather needs a lot of looking after. He needs someone to take care of him. So he's going to a holy place where he can spend his last days in peace.'

'Whereabouts?' the boy asked.

'Oh, a long way away. You wouldn't know if I told you.'

'Who's going to look after him?'

'Don't you bother about that,' said his mother. 'There will be someone to look after him all right. Now you keep out of my way. I'm very busy today.'

The boy's father didn't come home until late at night. He had a large, strong doko with him. After he had eaten he gave some food to the old man, then lifted him up and put him in the doko.

'What's this! What do you think you're doing?' cried the old man. 'Let me out!'

'Now, now!' his son said. 'You be quiet. It's all for your own good, I tell you. You know we can't look after you properly so we're taking you to a place where people can.'

'I don't believe you!' shouted the old man. 'You get me out of here.'

'Oh do please be quiet,' his daughter-in-law begged him. 'We're only doing what's best for you. You'll like it there.'

But the old man continued to shout.

'Liars! You want to get rid of me, that's what it is.'

He turned on his son.

'After all I've done for you,' he cried, 'and this is how you pay me back. You'll regret it, just you see if you don't!'

He shouted more and more.

The man ignored him. He set his lips tight and heaved the doko up on his back. The boy watched him as he opened the door to go.

'Father,' he said.

'What is it?' snapped his father.

'Father, when you've thrown grandfather away, please remember to bring the doko back.'

'Bring the doko back? What are you talking about?'

'The doko. Don't forget to bring it back because I'll need it when it's time to throw you away.'

His father stopped, turned round and came slowly back into the room. He put the doko down and started to lift the old man out.

retold by Robert Scott

Conkers

Mum was pleased with the new house because it was nearer Grandpa. She said it would be easier to 'keep an eye on him'. That meant making sure he put on clean socks and didn't upset the neighbours by playing his TV too loud.

Dad was pleased they'd moved to the new house because it had a bigger garden so he could grow vegetables (especially cabbage which was his favourite) and have a greenhouse for growing tomatoes.

Tim was pleased with the new house because the garden backed onto a wood. Not a Sherwood Forest-sized wood. Hardly a wood at all really, just a few trees and some brambles but the trees were brilliant for climbing. The best and biggest was a horse chestnut and it was just over the fence so Tim would always have his own supply of conkers falling straight into the garden.

The day they moved in Tim took Grandpa to see the wood. Grandpa said the horse chestnut tree was the best he'd ever seen.

'But one thing worries me, Grandpa,' said Tim. 'Suppose someone comes along and chops it down.'

'But why would they do that?' asked Grandpa. 'They'd be daft to spoil such a grand tree.

'For building,' said Tim. Dad says the wood is going to be built on soon. More houses. It might be in the way so they'd have to chop it down.'

'I don't think people can chop big trees down just like that,' said Grandpa. 'Leave it with me, I'll see what I can find out.'

Next day Grandpa went to the Council Offices and made some enquires. He returned smiling.

'No problem,' he said. 'There's something called a Tree Preservation Order on that horse chestnut. No-one's allowed to chop it down.'

'But what if they just went ahead anyway?' said Tim. The Council couldn't make them stick it back up again. That wouldn't work, not with a tree.'

'They'd be fined a huge amount of money,' said Grandpa. 'So much money that they wouldn't be able to afford to build houses after that. You can relax, Tim. Your horse chestnut is safe.'

And so it seemed. Dad planted the garden and grew so many cabbages that they had to eat cabbage every single day even after they'd stopped pretending it was their favourite vegetable. It was the same with the tomatoes. Dad's new greenhouse provided them with more tomatoes than they (and all the neighbours) could possibly eat.

One windy night in October, the year after they'd moved in, Tim was woken up by a strange noise. It was a sort of rumbling followed by a plink, plink, plink, SMASH. Then Tim noticed a sound like the roar of the sea. But they lived fifty miles from the coast. It was the wind. The wind had become so strong it was blowing the tiles off the roof. The tiles were plink, plink, plinking as they slid across other tiles before landing with a SMASH on the ground. Then there was an enormous CRASH and the sound of breaking glass. Tim had a horrible feeling that he knew what had caused such a large crash. He hoped he was wrong.

'Quick, downstairs,' said Tim's Mum. We'll be safer down there. It's blowing a gale. I'm worried in case the whole roof blows off. I hope Grandpa's all right.'

Grandpa had been woken by the rattle of dustbin lids blowing along the path. Every time one hit a parked car it made a great CLANG. He got up to make himself a cup of tea but the electricity was off. The gale had blown the power cables down. Every flat and house in the street was in darkness.

'I hope the family are all right,' thought Grandpa.

'I hope my greenhouse is all right,' thought Dad.

'I hope my horse chestnut is all right,' thought Tim. 'But I bet it isn't.'

As it grew light the wind died down. Tim's father drew back the curtains.

'Oh no,' he moaned. 'Just look at the greenhouse. That great big tree has fallen right across it.'

'That great big tree? Not my horse chestnut? Please don't let it be the horse chestnut,' prayed Tim. But it was. The horse chestnut was lying across what had until last night been Dad's greenhouse and was now a pile of broken glass and twisted metal smashed beyond repair.

Then Grandpa appeared.

Tim pointed to the fallen tree, conkers scattered all over the garden for the last time ever.

'That Tree Preservation Order, Grandpa. It didn't work did it?'

Grandpa put his arm round Tim's shoulders, 'We human beings can't control EVERYTHING in the world, Tim. We can try to stop people doing things they shouldn't like starting wars or being cruel to one another or even just chopping down beautiful trees but we can't control the wind and the damage it can do and we can't control the tides or the sun or the moon. We have to learn that some things can't be changed, we have to learn that we're not as powerful and important as sometimes we think we are. We have to learn to be humble.'

Then he added, 'We must try always to find the good things that come out of the bad.'

'Good things!' spluttered Tim. 'How can anything good come out of my horse chestnut being ruined?'

'It wasn't really YOUR horse chestnut, was it?' said Grandpa. It was growing on the other side of the fence and it was old and going rotten, that's why the wind was able to blow it down. But how would you like to have some trees that really do belong to you? A horse chestnut perhaps, even though it will be a few years before it has many conkers? You could have several different trees as well. You could plant them and look after them and see them grow. We could go down to the Garden Centre and choose some.'

'But where would we plant them?' asked Tim. 'There's only enough room for Dad's vegetables.'

'Not any more,' said Dad. You can have the cabbage patch. I think I'd rather see trees growing there. I don't think I'll want to see another cabbage for quite a long while. And when I get a new greenhouse I'll put it by the side of the house where it's more sheltered.

'See Tim', said Grandpa. 'Some things we really can change. Let's not fret about the storm damage, let's get started on clearing up the mess so we can plant those new trees.'

Tim started to feel better straight away. No point in worrying about things he couldn't change like fallen trees when there was something really important that he could be doing like planting new ones. Grandpa was right: Tim had found something good in a situation which had seen his worst fears come true. He began to make a list of all the trees he'd choose. Top of the list was, of course, horse chestnut.

Pauline Young

The man who loves elephants

The artist, David Shepherd, loves elephants. He calls them 'jumbos' and his paintings of them are famous all over the world.

The elephants he paints are African elephants, which are bigger than Indian ones. African elephants have huge, flapping ears, and tusks curving forward and upwards.

In some of the paintings they seem to be walking out of the picture towards you. Then you can almost feel their size and power.

But to David Shepherd they are not dangerous; they are gentle and intelligent beasts. Even so, he takes no foolish chances when making his pictures.

David has visited Africa many times and seen many elephants in the wild. However most of his paintings are finished in the studio, using careful notes of colours and hundreds of his own photographs and rough on-the-spot sketches.

He explains that it is too hot to paint out of doors, and that wet paint soon becomes covered in dust or dries on the palette. Once, when he was appearing in a television film, he was asked to set up his easel in the bush. The cameras were there when something made one of the elephants angry, causing her to charge. David Shepherd dropped his paints and ran!

Most African elephants today live in huge National Parks where they are protected. In the wild they are often killed by poachers for their valuable ivory tusks.

David once watched an elephant die slowly, killed by poisoned arrows. He has cried – and been angry – at what man is doing to wildlife and to the environment we all share and must pass on to future generations.

It was his horror at these killings which led him to raise thousands and thousands of pounds for conservation. As he is well-known for his animal paintings (lions, tigers and buffaloes, as well as elephants), David realised he could raise money by donating and auctioning some of his paintings. The very first picture he donated was of an elephant at a waterhole.

Then more and more people asked for his help. There was less and less time for his family and his painting. So in 1985 the David Shepherd Charitable Foundation was set up. Money goes mainly to the conservation charity, the WorldWide Fund for Nature (WWF) and the Young People's Trust for Endangered Species.

Year by year, the amount raised for conservation grows bigger. And year by year David Shepherd goes on painting. A long time ago he was painting pictures for Christmas cards. He says he soon got tired of painting all that snow but he has never got tired of painting his beloved 'jumbos'.

Anne English

The crowded house

There once lived a poor Jewish farmer named Yitzak who had a very large family, and lived in a very small hut. Yitzak's house was so crowded that his children had to take turns to sleep in the one tiny bed, and when everybody was in the house, hardly anyone could move.

At last Yitzak could stand it no longer. So he went to see the Rabbi to ask him what to do about this impossible situation.

The wise Rabbi thought hard and long, and at last he had an idea.

'I will tell you what to do,' he said. 'Bring your chicken to live with you inside the house.'
Yitzak couldn't understand how the chicken would help, but he trusted the Rabbi's wisdom and did as he was told. But as soon as the chicken was inside the house it grew frightened and flapped around the room, knocking Yitzak over and scattering its feathers everywhere.

So Yitzak went back to the Rabbi and complained. 'It only makes things worse,' he said.

'In that case,' said the Rabbi, 'bring in the goat to join your family and the chicken.'

Yitzak was even more confused, but did as he was told. Soon the goat was running around eating everything he could see. First he ate Yitzak's bedspread, and then he started on the children's clothes. Yitzak hurried back to the Rabbi.

'My house is more crowded than ever!' he cried.

'In that case bring in your cow to live with your family, the chicken and the goat.'

Yitzak couldn't understand what was going on at all, but he trusted the Rabbi's wisdom. So he went home and brought in the cow. But the huge cow immediately knocked over all the pots and pans and plates, and then stepped in the baby's cot. By now the house was so crowded that no one was able to move. They all had to press themselves against the wall so that Yitzak could squeeze past. Then he rushed off once more to see the Rabbi.

'Rabbi,' he cried, 'there is no room to breathe in my house. If it stays like this we will all go mad!'

'Don't worry,' said the Rabbi. 'I have another idea. Go home and take the chicken, the goat and the cow out of the house.'

Yitzak was completely puzzled and utterly bewildered, but he did as the Rabbi had said. He put all the animals back in the yard, and then an amazing thing happened. Without the animals the house seemed as big as a mansion. There was room now to breathe, to walk around, to play games, enough room for all his children, his wife and himself. So Yitzak and his family learned how to appreciate what they had, and they lived happily ever after in their huge little house.

Traditional Jewish tale

Promises, promises

I know I shouldn't have bought mum a plant for Christmas. No sooner was it through the front door than its days were numbered. It might just as well have carried a kill-by date.

Jessica said it was my fault for getting it half-price from the market on Christmas Eve. She said it must have been half dead when I bought it.

'Fancy waiting until the last minute,' she said.

But that was only because I'd stolen her idea. Anyway I wanted it to be a surprise.

My mum's a really good mum in lots of ways. She never seems to notice my untidy bedroom. One tidy up lasts about six months. She just throws my muddy football kit in the washing machine without moaning like Colin's mum does. And she always puts salt and vinegar crisps in my lunchbox. But she's useless with plants.

I'd picked this one specially. Despite what jealous Jessica said it was the healthiest Christmas cactus I'd ever seen. At the tip of each glossy green leaf hung a brilliant scarlet flower. I left the instruction card sticking prominently from the rich compost surrounding the plant, wrapped Christmassy paper round the pot and handed it over. 'Happy Christmas mum,' I said.

She seemed really pleased.

'Thanks Daniel. What a lovely thought. You know how I love flowers,' and she placed it proudly on the dining room table.

Jessica gave me a hate look from across the room. I enjoyed my moment of triumph but it was short-lived. By the end of December the leaves had lost their sheen and most of the flowers had dropped off.

My sister exacted her revenge.

'Lovely plant Daniel,' she mocked. 'Of course if you'd paid full price it would probably still be alive.'

Mum had followed the instructions carefully, but the cactus was decidedly sick.

On New Year's Day she moved it from its prime position to the kitchen windowsill. The next stop was the wheelie-bin. I couldn't let that happen. I felt responsible for the plant. And then I had a brainwave. Gran. If anyone could save it gran could. She's brilliant gran is. Jessica and I called her Wondergran. She can do anything. Repair my school trousers so you can't see the tear, make a meal out of nothing in five minutes, light a fire with paper sticks. Anything.

So I put the plant pot in a polythene bag and took it round to gran's flat. Mum didn't even notice it had gone.

'Your mother's never had green fingers Daniel. She's the only person I know who could put artificial flowers at risk,' gran said when I showed her the plant. She remembered it from Christmas Day. Looking at the brown, shrivelled leaves gran furrowed her brow before knocking off a few more dead flowers. Then she stuck the pot amongst the others in the front window. Surrounded by masses of green foliage it looked even more miserable.

'Will it recover?' I asked anxiously.

Gran stroked her nose with her finger and smiled.

'Definitely,' she said. 'I promise. But you rescued it in the nick of time.'

For the first few weeks I looked at the plant whenever I visited the flat. Gran hadn't thrown it away but I think she was just being kind. There were no signs of new growth. Wizened leaves poked up weakly through a solid block of soil. Gran was no miracle worker after all.

Why do people you trust always let you down? Like my teacher Mr Bramwell, the day I wore my glasses at school for the first time.

'Don't you worry about what people might say, Daniel,' he said confidently. 'If we don't make a fuss no-one will even notice , I promise you.'

So what happened?

The lesson was only five minutes old when the headmaster came into the classroom with a message for me.

'Is Daniel here?' he asked, loudly from the door.

Before anyone could answer it was out.

'Oh there he is. I didn't recognise him in his glasses.'

So everyone stared across, nudging and pointing.

Mr Bramwell was fidgeting uncomfortably at his desk. It wasn't his fault, but you shouldn't make promises you can't keep.

I didn't bother to look at the plant anymore. And after a month or two I forgot all about it.

On Christmas morning we all sat in the dining room opening presents.

I'd played safe this year and bought mum a bottle of perfume and a posh hanky. Jessica had splashed out on a compact disc, dad bought earrings and gran settled for chocolates. So who had been daft enough to buy her the plant? The plant with the glossy leaves and brilliant scarlet flowers, that she'd placed proudly in the centre of the table. I looked across at gran. Surely it wasn't .....

She read my thoughts.

'You've a lot to learn Daniel,' she said, 'and I don't just mean about plants either.'

Liz Lawman

Just a pile of rice

There was once a carpenter who lived in China, his name
was Master Xhang and he made all sorts of things out of wood.
He made beds and sheds and plates and gates.
He made tables for ladies and cradles for babies.
He made houses for everyone in the town.

One day, the people asked him to build something very special.
They wanted a new temple.

'It must be strong,' they said, 'so it will last a long time.
It must be beautiful so people will want to visit it.
And it must be ready in time for the festival.'

The people wanted the new temple to have a high roof
made of sandstone, and held up by four wooden pillars.

Master Xhang set about the building work.

He had carpenters to make the pillars tall and strong.
He had stonemasons to cut the sandstone roof
out of the hillside.
They chipped away with sharp tools
until the roof was the right shape and size.
Then they set about making beautiful carvings
all over the surface.

The building work took months. Everyday, Master Xhang
went to watch the carpenters and stonemasons at work,
and gave them advice.

All the men in the town cleared the ground.
They made a base, with holes for the pillars to stand in.
The carpenters worked nearby, planning and drawing,
measuring and sawing, until the pillars were ready.
They lifted them and stood them upright in their holes,
ready for the roof to go on top.
The stonemasons were there too, tapping and splitting,
cutting and chipping, until the roof was finished.

It was very hard work, and it took a long time.

At last, on the day before the festival,
the whole job was done, except for putting on the heavy roof.
The men all stood around it.
They bent down and put their hands underneath to try and lift it.

'One ... two ... three ... *lift*,' said Master Xhang.

Nothing happened. The sandstone roof didn't move.

The men looked at each other. They shifted their feet a little, and took a deep breath.

'One ... two ... three ... *heave*,' said Master Xhang.
Nothing happened. It was no good. The sandstone roof was too heavy.

'We just can't shift it,' said the men. 'If we can't even lift it, how are we going to get it up onto those pillars?'

Master Xhang thought long and hard, but he couldn't find the answer.
All the carpenters and the stonemasons thought too,
but no-one had any idea what to do.

'It's no good,' they all said. 'We'll just have to have the festival without our new temple. It won't be the same, but there's nothing we can do.' One by one they packed up their tools and went home.

Master Xhang took one last look at the unfinished temple
and turned to go home. On his way, he passed through the market.
People were rushing to do their last-minute shopping for the festival.
The shops were all beautifully decorated and piled high with
party food, fireworks and decorations.

Master Xhang sighed. 'Everyone has worked very hard.
I was sure that the temple would be complete, but now
I've let the whole town down. This is hopeless.
No-one can solve this problem, except perhaps Lu Ban,
the god of all carpenters.

Master Xhang went sadly home, and puzzled over the problem,
but he couldn't find an answer.

Suddenly, there was a knock at the door.
Master Xhang went to answer it, and found a stranger standing there.

'I'm a carpenter and stonemason,' said the stranger.
'I've travelled a long way. Can I come in and rest for a while?'

'Why, I'm a carpenter too,' said Master Xhang in surprise.
'Come in and eat with us, and we'll have a chat about work.'

The stranger came in and sat down. Master Xhang's wife
put bowls and chopsticks on the table
and brought the rice which she'd cooked.

'This food looks wonderful,' said the stranger.
'We need some good wine to go with it.'
'That's a very good idea,' said Master Xhang. 'You wait here
while I go out and fetch a bottle.'

When he got back, the stranger wasn't there! Master Xhang
ran to the door and looked up and down the street,
but he was nowhere to be seen.

'He's disappeared into thin air!' he exclaimed to his wife.

'But look what he's done to the dinner!' cried Mrs Xhang
in horror. 'It's a complete mess.'

Master Xhang looked. Then he stared. His eyes opened wide
in amazement, and he laughed out loud.

'It's the temple!' he shouted, and danced around the room.

'What?' asked his wife.

All she could see was a pile of rice,
and four wooden chopsticks.
Her delicious dinner was a ruined heap on the table.
She couldn't imagine how a spoilt dinner
could make him dance with joy.
'What are you so happy about?' she demanded.

'Now I know how we can put the roof on the temple,'
laughed Master Xhang.

Master Xhang rushed out of the house and called all the people together.
'Quick, get your spades and follow me,' he yelled.
'We'll get that roof on after all.'

The men were surprised, but they did what he asked.

At the temple, Master Xhang explained what they had to do.
All night long the men worked. They dug earth
and carried it to the temple, where they emptied it
on the floor. They piled the earth higher and higher,
until it covered the wooden pillars. Then they made a
ramp from the ground right up to the top of the pile.

'Now for the roof,' said Master Xhang.

The men left the pile of earth
and went over to the beautiful sandstone roof. They fetched ropes
and tied them around it. They gripped the ropes, took a deep breath,
bent their knees and got ready.

'One ... two ... three ... *pull*!' said Master Xhang.
This time the roof began to move. It was far too heavy to lift,
but the men could just manage to pull it along the ground.
They dragged it up the ramp. Up and up it went,
right to the top of the pile of earth.

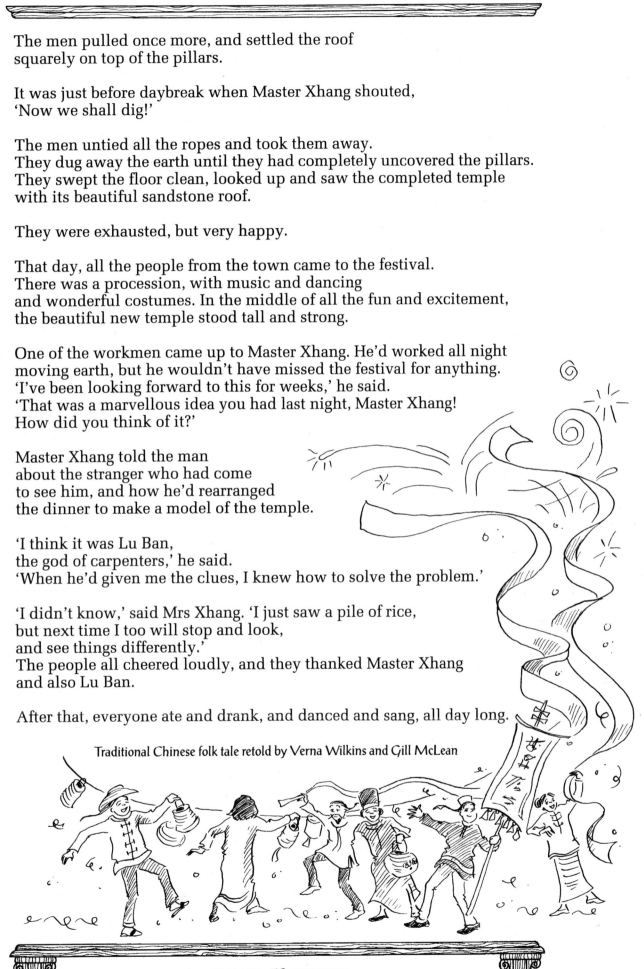

The men pulled once more, and settled the roof
squarely on top of the pillars.

It was just before daybreak when Master Xhang shouted,
'Now we shall dig!'

The men untied all the ropes and took them away.
They dug away the earth until they had completely uncovered the pillars.
They swept the floor clean, looked up and saw the completed temple
with its beautiful sandstone roof.

They were exhausted, but very happy.

That day, all the people from the town came to the festival.
There was a procession, with music and dancing
and wonderful costumes. In the middle of all the fun and excitement,
the beautiful new temple stood tall and strong.

One of the workmen came up to Master Xhang. He'd worked all night
moving earth, but he wouldn't have missed the festival for anything.
'I've been looking forward to this for weeks,' he said.
'That was a marvellous idea you had last night, Master Xhang!
How did you think of it?'

Master Xhang told the man
about the stranger who had come
to see him, and how he'd rearranged
the dinner to make a model of the temple.

'I think it was Lu Ban,
the god of carpenters,' he said.
'When he'd given me the clues, I knew how to solve the problem.'

'I didn't know,' said Mrs Xhang. 'I just saw a pile of rice,
but next time I too will stop and look,
and see things differently.'
The people all cheered loudly, and they thanked Master Xhang
and also Lu Ban.

After that, everyone ate and drank, and danced and sang, all day long.

Traditional Chinese folk tale retold by Verna Wilkins and Gill McLean

In, over, through, off

When I was a little boy, long before you were born, I went to the village school in West Wylam, overlooking the River Tyne. There were fifty of us in one big classroom, boys and girls between four and seven. I had to walk with my brothers two miles up a steep hill from our village to get to West Wylam. They were in the Big Boys' school and I was in the Mixed Infants' school.

In the Infants we all had to learn to knit on Monday mornings. All except Foster Newton and I'll tell you about him later. The knitting started at five past nine and finished at a quarter past ten. Its proper name was Plain Knitting but we called it In, Over, Through, Off. Knitting is very complicated, as you will see.

First of all Mrs Armstrong cast on for you: that is, she put a row of stitches on your left-hand needle. When she called 'In' you had to poke your right-hand needle into the end stitch on the left hand needle, leave go of it, grab the wool and loop a bit of it over the point of the needle you had just let go of. That was when she called 'Over'. It was very difficult. Then she shouted 'Through' and 'Off' but the actions are too complicated for me to explain in words, even though I can still remember how to do it after sixty years.

The real problem was that the girls could already knit before they came to school. A bit like skipping. Their mothers taught them. They didn't teach the boys because in those days boys didn't learn cooking and washing dishes and that sort of thing. They just played in the woods from morning till night.

May be that's why Mrs Armstrong didn't like boys very much, except Foster Newton of course. She let the girls bring their own wool of any colour but she gave 'the boys' some old red wool with wrinkles in it where it had been pulled out from old jerseys; by the time we'd had it for two years it was dark grey.

Anyhow, at five past nine, Mrs Armstrong told Joanie Clarke and Connie Callender to give out the boys' knitting. They were the best knitters; they probably became prison warders or slave drivers when they grew up. After that Mrs Armstrong shouted:

'Balls of wool on right knees!
Left-hand needle, grasp!
Right-hand needle, ready!
Connie and Joanie, begin!'

They began to call out and we all joined in, except Foster Newton:

'In, over, through, off, in, over, through, off.'

Not so bad at first when you were fresh, but then the terrible two decided to speed up the count. I'll tell you something you won't know unless you can knit: as soon as you start to rush you panic and your hands get clumsy and the loops get tight and you cannot poke your needle under them when they shout 'In!' so you split the strands of wool and Mrs Armstrong comes over to poke you with her ruler and tells you that your fingernails are disgusting and you'd better stay in at playtime Jack Welch to pull that awful knitting out. Whack!

That was it. One by one the boys gave up in despair while the girls continued to make beautiful pixie hoods and tea-cosies that were a credit to West Wylam Infants' School. As they skipped out to play in the yard, Joanie Clarke and Connie Callender brought in Mrs Armstrong's cup of tea and the boys pulled out their awful knitting ready for a fresh start next Monday. After two years of this torture I left to go into the Big Boys and took my knitting home as a present for my mother. It was five inches long, four inches at the bottom and two inches at the top. My mother said I was a clever lad and used it to block up a knot hole in the back door.

I promised to tell you about Foster Newton. He was supposed to be simple: he couldn't read and he did not talk very clearly. What he liked best was standing on his hands against a gate watching the horses go by upside down. He was Mrs Armstrong's pet. So when we were at the knitting Foster was allowed to play with his Plasticine. He had his own tin and his own board and his own skewer and he used to warm the clay on the radiators or under his armpits or even in his mouth on cold Mondays. He could make he most marvellous motor-bikes, like the one his father used to ride to the pit. He never made anything else, just a perfect model motor-bike which took him a whole hour. Then he lumbered up to Mrs Armstrong's table balancing his board like a waiter's tray. He grunted loudly to attract her attention.

'Stop knitting! And stop cheering you boys!

Eee! Foster That's lovely pet. You are an example to these terrible lads. What is he you boys?'

'He's an example to us Mrs Armstrong.'

'Now bonny lad, here's something for you (and she popped a sweet into his great grinning mouth). I want you to go round the school and show your motor bike to the other bairns.'

Off Foster went to the other classes in the Big School. When he returned his trouser pockets were bulging with toffees.

'Now put it away pet and then go out to play while these bad boys pull their knitting out.'

We watched him swagger out, grunting away to himself and we all wondered if he really was the simple one of West Wylam.

John Welch

Ben's flowers

It was the worst possible start. Rain pouring the whole journey. Mum and Dad bickering as they tried to keep close behind the furniture van. My sister Jen feeling sick, sitting next to me in the back of the car. And then Ben's accident.

I'd known as soon as I'd heard the squeal of brakes. Someone had left the front door open in all the comings and goings and now Ben was dead. We'd been in our new house for just two hours.

I'd never wanted to move anyway. What's the good of a house if it's on a main road? A busy main road with tanker lorries, like the one that killed Ben.

'You won't hear the traffic through the double-glazed windows,' Dad had said. I didn't need to hear it to know it was there. I'd never forget it was there. It would always be there. But Ben wouldn't.

He had always been around. When Jen and I got home from school he'd meet us at the gate, bounding up, licking our hands. We'd drop our school bags in the porch and take him for a walk. Or rather he'd take us, dragging up behind him as he strained at the lead eager to reach the field at the back of our old house.

Once there he'd run in huge circles, gradually closing until he was nipping at our heels. We were sheep and he was rounding us up. Then he'd lie panting on the grassy bank at the top of the field, pink tongue bright against black jaws.

'Ben!' I shouted, hearing the squeal of brakes. Panicking with sudden, certain knowledge I raced out of the room. Jen, catching my desperation, ran after me.

The tanker lorry was slewed across the road, front wheels straddling the grass verge. I turned my back to avoid the sight of Ben's crumpled, lifeless body.

Dad pulled me towards him, his arms sheltering me. I struggled to free myself, lashing out with clenched fists, tasting tears, sobbing uncontrollably. Dad held me, talking softly, speaking Ben's name. I was just aware of Mum clutching Jen, their heads buried together.

At last Mum, Jen and I went back inside our new house and Dad went down to the road.

I'd loved my old house, my old street, my old school.

We didn't even get an extra holiday. We moved in the half-term break. Our new school was huge. All concrete and glass with long corridors and shiny plastic tiled floors.

Three hundred children, and I didn't know one of them.

Sometimes we'd had new kids at my old school. You had to be nice to them, show them round, where the toilets were, stuff like that. But nobody could really help them: they had to help themselves.

Some fitted in straight away. Others took ages. You'd find them crying quietly in the cloakroom at lunch-times. I'd never really thought about it before. New teachers, different rules. Everybody knowing everything and you finding out one thing at a time.

That's what I was thinking about when I heard the squeal of brakes. And then I forgot all about it. I just thought of Ben.

Dad came in looking tired. He cleared his throat and sat on one of the unopened boxes.

'He wouldn't have known anything about it,' he began, 'it would have all been over before he felt anything ...'

'For goodness sake shut up Dad,' I thought. 'How do you know what Ben felt?' Tears began welling up. I wasn't listening to Dad anymore. He was talking and rummaging in the boxes like a mad thing. Then he was holding something in front of my face. Spread in the palms of his hand were some wizened brown bulbs. Like onions. And he was still talking.

'I'll get the car out and we'll go back to our old house.'

'Back to our old house?'

If only we could. If only we could go back to this morning. I'd hold Ben so tight ...

'And we'll plant them in the field. On that grassy bank where you used to play.'

What was he talking about? Plant bulbs in a field?

Dad went into the field on his own. We waited in the car until he'd got the unpleasant business over, then trudged across the wet grass to join him. We all scraped up clumps of grass and pressed the bulbs into the soft earth beneath. We worked silently. I still didn't really understand why we were there.

That night in my bedroom I counted cracks in the ceiling. Cars, sounding like supercharged bees, buzzed constantly along the road outside.

Jen sat on my bed. For a girl she didn't cry much.

'It can only get better Simon,' she said.

In the morning I'd get up early and walk down to look at the new school. On my own.

It was Spring when we went back to our old house. The new people had changed the garden. They'd turfed our vegetable plot and put a rotary clothes line in the middle.

Worst still they'd put up a high fence out the back. It wasn't the same anymore. I bet they'd scraped off my wallpaper and taken down my bookshelves.

As soon as we got to the field I knew what Dad had meant.

We could see the yellow trumpeted flowers from the gate. They were Ben's flowers.

And we could come back and see them every year.

Ian Addis

The Asrai

I have not told this story to many people. I will tell you, but perhaps you should not speak of it to anyone else. It is a strange story and not everyone would believe it. I know the truth.

In the north of the country, there is a great lake. It is clear and deep, and rich in fish, but no-one fishes there. A lake as deep as that has secrets. Every day, the fishermen would go further north, making a longer journey, rather than fish in its still waters. No-one even spoke of the lake until the young man came.

'Are there no fish in the lake?'

'Yes. Good fish, they say, and many of them,' replied the fishermen.

'Then why not fish there instead of going further off?'

Nobody would answer at first. They looked away or spoke of other things. At last, one old man took him aside, speaking quietly.

'The lake you speak of has never been fished by our people. There are stories from the past. It is very deep, very still, fringed with reeds and full of peace. Perfect, in fact, for the Asrai.'

'The Asrai?' asked the young man. 'What do you mean?'

'I have never seen them myself,' said the old man, 'but my grandfather knew something of them. He would never tell us the full story, but I remember his eyes when he said the name – deep, grey and sad like the lake. The Asrai are the people of the lake. They live in its depths, rarely visiting the surface. Their hair is green and their skin sparkles and changes colour like the water. My grandfather said that they do not seek to harm us, and yet he feared them, I think.

The young man smiled. 'You do not fish a perfectly good lake because your grandfather said there were people living at the bottom? Are you serious? Surely you do not believe such a story!'

'I believe,' said the old man. 'There have been – incidents. Perhaps I should not have told you. The Asrai are dangerous, even to think about. Put all thought of them out of your mind. Come with us to the far lake and be happy.

But the young man laughed aloud and walked away.

From that time, the young man fished in the great lake and had wonderful luck. Every night, he would push his boat out through the reeds and glide across the still water. At dawn, he would return, many fish filling his baskets. He had to sell them in the distant town. In the village by the lake, no-one would buy the fish which belonged to the Asrai.

His good fortune lasted all the summer, but one night the air felt sharp and brown leaves lay in his path. The lake was as still as ever but it no longer sparkled. The reeds, stiffened perhaps by a tinge of frost, held him back for a moment as if in warning. But to the young man, it meant nothing. All night long he fished and, as the sky began to pale, he pulled in a loaded net. There seemed to be weed floating in the net, but then the young man understood. He looked closer. It was long, green hair. He had caught an Asrai.

The Asrai was a young woman. Her skin glittered and her hands and feet were delicately webbed. But her eyes! They were deep like the lake, as grey as the coming morning and so sad. He thought she spoke. He could not tell if it was the Asrai or the rippling movement of the lake. In his head, the sound said, 'Let the Asrai go. Return the Asrai to the lake.'

He hesitated, then looked firmly towards the shore. He would be famous. He would show her to everyone and be well paid for it. He no longer thought of the Asrai, only of himself. He leaned over the side and pulled her aboard. As he did so, a pain scorched his hand. Although her touch was cool, it was almost as if it had burned him. She, too, shrank from his human warmth and the rising sun. Because she seemed to fear the daylight, he threw some reeds over her in the bottom of the boat, and pulled hard for the shore.

He reached the end of the lake just as the sun rose. He felt well satisfied with his catch, and threw off the covering reeds. The Asrai was not there. His net was empty. In the bottom of the boat there was nothing but a pool of lake water.

Ever after, the hand which had touched the Asrai was icy cold, and yet, it was marked, as if it had been passed through fire.

As I say, perhaps we should not speak further of this. These days, people do not know of the Asrai, but I know the truth. If I took off my glove you would understand.

Traditional English folk tale retold by Pat Thomson

Raymond

People said Raymond was 'Backward'.

He couldn't read very well. He could hardly write at all. When everybody else had finished their work, he'd only written about two lines.

Eventually, Raymond was put in the class for Slow Learners. Sometimes it was called the Opportunity Class or the Compensatory Teaching Unit or the Remedial Class.

Whatever it was called by the school, as far as Raymond's mates were concerned it was for the Duffers – the Thickies.

One day, a very important man came to visit the school – one of Her Majesty's inspectors.

He was impressed by what he saw. The technology lesson was especially to his liking. The children were solving very difficult problems involving weights and pulleys and intricate pieces of machinery. They were 'using information technology to explore patterns and relationships and to form and test simple hypotheses' according to the teacher.

The inspector wasn't sure what the teacher meant but he said 'Well done.'

He was equally impressed by the computer department. All sorts of problem solving and decision making at the press of a button.

The design technology group were designing the Car of the Future.

'Very imaginative. Good work' said the inspector.

He was beaming as he left the school at the end of the day.

His expression quickly changed when he saw his car.

He had parked it on the road opposite the school. It had a puncture in one of its wheels.

He jacked his car up and undid the nuts on the wheel with the flat tyre.

He placed the nuts of the edge of the kerb. He walked back to the car with his spare wheel and then, to his horror, he accidentally kicked the nuts into a drain.

Gone! Disappeared! Six feet down and no hope of recovery.

Now Her Majesty's inspector was a very clever gentleman with a university degree. But he had absolutely no idea what to do. He wondered if he should return to the technology department for some help.

Raymond had been watching this little scene with interest.

'I can see you're in trouble, sir' he said.

'Yes,' replied the Inspector. 'I certainly am.'

'Can I make a suggestion?' said Raymond.

'Of course,' replied the inspector with a condescending smile.

'Why don't you take one nut off each of the other three wheels and put them on your spare? That way, you'll have three nuts on each wheel. At least it will get you to a garage where you can buy some new ones.'

The inspector smiled at Raymond, with admiration.

'Brilliant!' he said. 'Absolutely brilliant. Are you a pupil at this school?'

'I am. I'm in the class for the slow kids. I may be backward, but I'm not stupid.'

C. Oglethorpe

ST

Toby stared miserably through the window of the tiny cottage he shared with his brother Ben. There were stones to clear from the land before ploughing could start. Fences needed mending, walls rebuilding. The house was in a dreadful state. Years of neglect by parents too poor and too ill to maintain it had left the building damp, cold and uncomfortable.

Was this the best that life could offer?

Years of labour, toil and sweat. Toby knew there was an easier way to make a living.

And he told Ben later that day.

Ben agreed. He always agreed. They were alike in so many ways. They looked alike, thought alike, acted alike. And hadn't they practised as little boys, stealing apples from neighbours' orchards, sneaking things from village shops, too clever to be caught?

But what to steal? They lived in a tiny village thirty miles from the nearest town. Just a cluster of cottages, a few shops, an inn and a whitewashed church surrounded by green fields. There were no banks to rob and most of the villagers were just as poor as themselves.

So they began stealing sheep. First for their own meat and later to sell to a dishonest butcher in a neighbouring village. But secrets are hard to keep in a small community. The brothers ate a little too well and flaunted their new found wealth in the inn. People began to talk, and soon their sheep stealing days were numbered.

Arrested, they were taken together to face trial in town. They had no hope of being found innocent or of receiving a lenient punishment. There were no lenient punishments. The penalty for sheep stealing was often death.

This time, however, the magistrate showed mercy. Of a kind. The brothers were sentenced to three years imprisonment. But first they were taken into the prison yard and branded with a red hot iron. First Ben, arms tied to his sides, was held down next to the fire. A branding iron, usually reserved to mark cattle, was heated in the flames and then pressed on his forehead.

The air filled with the smell of burnt flesh.

Watching, Toby could feel his brother's pain. Then it was his turn. The letters burned into their foreheads were S T. Sheep Thief.

The time in prison passed slowly. Days in hard labour, nights sleeping on straw pallets on a stone floor in a cell that was freezing in winter, stifling in summer. Their only consolation was in being together and together they planned the future. A life of crime was over. They intended to 'go straight' and make a new start. But where? Everyone in their own village knew of the past. Wouldn't it be better to travel miles away, abroad even?

Ben thought so.

'Think of the lands we can see and the money we can make,' he said, as the day of their release grew near. 'We're both young and strong and willing to work. Why stay here where everyone sneers at the scars on your head and hides the silver when you walk in?'

Toby felt differently.

'I'll be sorry to be parted from you, Ben', he replied, 'but I've a craving to see the old village again and sleep in the little cottage if it's still standing. No doubt it'll be hard but that's what I'll do. At least you'll know where to find me when you come back loaded with money and a foreign wife.'

On their release from prison the brothers were separated for the first time in their lives.

Ben became a merchant seaman. He enjoyed the travel but not the company. The other sailors were rough and troublesome. Many were criminals. Ben had no wish to go back to jail so he left the sea and tried to settle in a foreign country. As the shores of his new land approached, shining in the sun like a golden promise, his heart lifted.

Things turned out to be harder than expected. The same question everywhere he went in his search for work. 'What are those strange marks on your head?'

Although no-one understood their meaning they knew that only criminals were branded.

Ben survived through seasonal work. Fruit picking, harvesting, ploughing, sowing. But the rest of his life was spent wandering from place to place without ever finding a home. He often thought of Toby, but sadly as he had never learned to write was unable to contact his brother ever again.

Toby had returned to his own village. A village where he was a known criminal. At first he was an outcast, shunned by people who did not seek the company of a thief. But Toby stuck it out. Reviving old skills learned as a boy he rebuilt the derelict cottage, thatched the roof and tended the land. Single-handed. No-one helped or gave advice. News of his skill and diligence quickly impressed the villagers but it was a much slower process to win their trust. That took years. He comforted the sick and elderly, lent a hand in delivering a difficult foal, worked unceasingly on the church roof when it was damaged in a gale and left his own field at harvest time to search for a missing child. Such kindnesses and honesty were finally rewarded.

Accepted at last, Toby married the Miller's daughter and together they raised a family.

Time passed and the scars on his forehead faded.

No-one thought any more of them than they thought about the innkeeper's baldness, the blacksmith's red nose or the black wart on the baker's wife's chin.

Many years later a stranger in the village noticed a grey haired man smoking his pipe in the square. He asked one of the children who the old man was and what the letters on his forehead meant. The child did not know, had never thought about it but, wishing to be helpful, she considered for a while and then said.

'I don't know but it must be something nice for he's the kindest of men, very wise, helpful and religious. Perhaps ST stands for saint.'

Mike Hoy

Wildlife

'Now class, come and sit on the carpet,' called Miss Ladwa, 'I've got some exciting news. Anthony!' she called to the last boy to make a move, 'hurry up or you'll miss it, won't you?'

As slowly as he dared, Anthony crossed the classroom and sat himself on the very edge of the carpet, so that most of his bottom was still on the cold, hard floor. The hard edge of the carpet quickly began to hurt.

'Anthony, you're keeping everyone waiting and it's not fair on the others, is it? Now sit properly.' He wriggled onto the carpet as the whole class turned round to stare at him. Anthony could not really say why he behaved like this. In lots of ways he wanted to be just like everyone else in the class, but he wasn't. He didn't know why, but he found it so hard to remember things. Sometimes, when Miss Ladwa was able to sit down with him and explain things properly, he would find them easier but it never seemed to last. The next day, it was no better than before. No one else seemed to have this problem. It was all right for them.

'As you know,' Miss Ladwa was saying, 'now that Mr Newbold has retired, he is not going to look after the school pond any more and so we thought it would be a lovely idea if each class took it in turn.' There was a buzz of excitement around the room. 'Now, I've just been speaking to the head and she wants our class to go first.'

The next day, after play in the afternoon, work on the pond began. Miss Ladwa decided that one group of children could go out each day. Anthony was put in the first group with Jacko and Sahel, two boys he often played football with, and the two girls who were the best in the class at almost everything, Annie and Dipika. Dipika was all right, Anthony quite liked her but Annie was different altogether. She lived on a farm a few miles away and all she could talk about were *her* horses and *her* sheep. It got everyone down, even Dipika sometimes.

Miss Ladwa got the group together and gave them their instructions.

'Today the best thing would be to do a survey of the pond. Have a look at the state of the water and see if the pond itself needs cleaning.' The group turned to go. 'Oh, and why don't you also do a survey of the long grass between the pond and the road. See what signs of wild life you can find.'

When they got to the pond, Annie and Dipika immediately started noting things down on their clipboards and Jacko and Sahel decided they would count the number of fish, even though the water was so murky it was difficult to see anything.

'What about you, Anthony,' said Dipika, 'what do you want to do?'

'Dunno,' said Anthony, with the slightest flick of his head and shoulders. Miss Ladwa had learned to dread that gesture.

'You've got to do something,' said Dipika cheerfully, 'Miss said we had to work together and help each other. What about collecting all the litter?'

'What about it?' asked Anthony.

'Well, all right then, do a survey of the long grass and see what you can find.'

Without a word, Anthony turned and walked away from the pond, his hands in his pockets, kicking the tufts of long grass as he went. What he was looking for, he had no idea.

Some way from the pond, Anthony's foot kicked against something. It was an empty oil can which someone had thoughtlessly thrown over the hedge from the nearby road. Anthony stooped down to pull up the can, and as he did so, two baby frogs started up in fright. Anthony stooped down and picked up one of them before it could escape and, cupping it in two hands, he ran back to the others. Just at that moment, Miss Ladwa was walking over to see how they were getting on.

'Look what I've got, Miss,' he called.

'What is it, Anthony?' she asked as everyone gathered around.

'Come on, Ant, what you got? Show us,' urged Jacko. Anthony slowly removed his top hand, trying not to frighten the little frog. The group was now so close, their heads were nearly touching. From the corner of his eye, he could see Annie watching closely but, unlike the others, she had a kind of sneer on her face, a look which told Anthony she would never admit that he could ever have anything good.

Suddenly, he jerked the hand with the frog right up into Annie's face. She screamed, swung her arm upwards knocking Anthony's hand away. The little frog flew into the air, landing several feet away on the hard footpath. Anthony dashed over to where the baby frog lay completely still on the tarmac. As the group followed to see what had happened, Anthony lashed out at Annie, hitting her hard on the shoulder. She turned away, crying.

'Anthony, go indoors at once,' ordered Miss Ladwa, sternly. 'You are not to hit people like that. Go and wait by my desk.'

With tears in his eyes, Anthony turned to go in. For a second something had gone right for him. But it hadn't lasted. Annie had spoilt it for him and he hated her. As he entered the classroom, everyone seemed to stop and look at him. He didn't care how he was punished. Just at that minute he didn't care about anything.

When Miss Ladwa came back into the classroom she asked everyone to pack up quickly because it was home time. When the classroom had emptied, Anthony was still standing by the desk but his teacher was clearly in a hurry.

'Anthony,' she said, 'how many times have I told you not to hit other people?' Anthony said nothing. Miss Ladwa looked at her watch. 'Look,' she said, 'I can't stop now, I'll deal with this in the morning.'

Anthony followed his teacher slowly out of the classroom. Already the school was quiet, except for the hum of a distant vacuum cleaner. His path took him past the pond and he stopped. Someone had piled all the leaves in a soggy heap near the water's edge next to a disgusting heap of decomposing litter – crisp packets and sweet wrappers of all kinds.

Suddenly, Anthony remembered his baby frog and he went to the spot where it had fallen but it was nowhere to be seen. He wondered whether someone might have thrown its little body on to the flower bed by the side of the path but it wasn't there either. His frog had gone.

At once, his anger returned. All his feelings of being different, of being looked down on by the others, of being no good, flooded back. He ran to the piles of rubbish and kicked them as hard as he could, scattering them back across the water. Then he raced over to the oil can, where he had first found his frog. Not caring whether he was seen or not, he threw the can into the pond as hard as he could. As it filled with water, the can began to sink, slowly at first then much quicker until it disappeared with a gurgle. Anthony stared at the water until it became still again and then, as the first rainbow traces of oil appeared on the surface he turned to go.

Not feeling anything at all, he walked on. As he reached the school gate, Dipika was waiting for him.

'Anthony,' she called, 'I've got something for you.' To his delight Anthony saw in her hands his baby frog.

'After you were sent in, it began to move,' she said, 'so I put it in some grass and wrapped it in my cardigan until home time.' Then she added, 'I knew you were upset.'

Anthony did not know what to say. That someone had thought about him and his feelings made him feel, somehow, that he mattered. Then he remembered the pond and suddenly he realised what he had done. Grabbing the frog with a quick 'Thanks', he raced back into school.

By now the oil was spreading, unstoppably, across the water. The leaves and litter lay still on the surface but there, in the middle of the pond, just as Anthony had feared, floated the upturned bodies of two dead fish.

Don Rowe

Runaway

Jody couldn't wait to get home. She went out of the cloakroom door, across the car park and rushed up the school drive. She wanted to see her mum.

'If I take a short cut through the spinney I'll get home more quickly,' she thought.

So she hurried along the muddy tree-lined track that brought her out near a row of shops, raced past a dog tied to a post outside the supermarket, dodged between two pushchairs on the pavement near the hairdressers and crossed over the road behind a milk-float parked against the kerb.

She'd been worried all morning. All through lessons words and figures had jumbled together in her head. Her mum was ill. She must be very ill if she hadn't gone to work. She never missed work.

'I think I'll stay at home today,' she'd said. 'I'm not feeling too good this morning.'

Mrs Cooper, next door, had taken Jody to school with the twins.

Perhaps her mum had gone back to bed. She imagined her, all snuggled up in the sheets, pale and shivery. There was no-one to look after her. What if she'd come over all dizzy and fallen over and bumped her head and was lying at the bottom of the stairs...?

'Come on Jody,' Miss Cave said quietly. Jody hadn't heard the playtime bell. The rest of the class were filing out into the cloakroom. 'You can finish that later,' the teacher said. The picture came back into her mind as she approached the main road. What if her mum had lain there all morning? Unable to move. Paralysed.

Jody glanced down the road, quickly to the left, quickly to the right before shooting across between the traffic.

Nearly home now. At the front gate she stopped in surprise. Her mum was in the garden hanging out washing. Words formed in her head. 'Mu....' she began. Then stopped. What would her mum say?

'What are you doing here? You ought to be at school. Did you cross the main road on your own?'

Jody ducked down quickly behind the hedge. Her mum mustn't see her. No-one must see her. She had to get back to school before anyone realised she'd gone.

The road was busy. A stream of cars and lorries and buses and motor bikes raced past. Whoosh! She hadn't noticed before. She'd just hurried across without thinking. This time she did it properly. The Green Cross Code way. She looked all around and listened. When it was clear she walked across. She didn't run like before. She might trip. The thought made her go cold all over.

Katie's mum was outside her house talking to the milkman. Jody crossed over to avoid being seen but it meant she had to pass the row of shops. There was no other way to go. The dog was still tied up outside the supermarket. It seemed to have grown and filled the pavement now, half wolf – half tyrannosaurus – sharp yellow teeth, slavering jaws. She closed her eyes and squeezed past expecting the dog to pounce any second.

There were no shouts from the playground. Playtime was over. The

children had gone back into school. What could Jody do? She couldn't go home, her mum would be upset. But she couldn't go back to school either. Mr Spring the headmaster would be angry and everyone would stare and point and tease. Soon they'd realise she'd gone and come looking. Perhaps they already were.

Why not hide in the spinney? No-one would find her there. Inside the wood it was dark and gloomy. No sunlight could find a way through the thick canopy of leaves and branches overhead. Brambles scratched her legs. Twigs poked painfully into her face. And there were the noises. Whining, crackling, hissing, scuttling. She shouldn't have left the path. She was safe on the path. Her socks felt wet through her shoes. She wanted to cry, to shout out. That's when she heard the footsteps. Far off at first, but getting closer. Someone was coming. She huddled against a tree, pressing her face against the rough bark. Images appeared before her eyes: her indoor shoes hanging on the peg, her friends turning away as they went into the playground, herself waiting behind, then opening the cloakroom door before crossing the car park and hurrying up the drive. To see her mum. Her mum who wasn't ill at all. It was like a dream. A nightmare. But these people were real enough. There were two of them standing on the path looking across at her.

'It's alright, Jody'.

Miss Cave's words were soft and gentle but her face was creased with worry. Mr Spring said nothing. He would have plenty to say later.

Together they walked slowly back towards school.

Ian Addis

Yan's first voyage

Yan was sixteen when he left the north of Scotland.

'I hope you don't regret this,' his mother said but there was no room for regret. He was full of excitement.

The night he left he was so busy, checking and packing, that in the end he had to run for the train.

He only just managed to scramble on board before the guard blew the whistle and the train pulled away from the platform.

All his family were there to see him off and as Yan waved through the windows, he wondered when he would see them again.

The journey to England took for ever and it was three in the morning when the train pulled into Liverpool, but even though it was so early, Liverpool was wide awake.

Yan found the docks easily. The lights and the noise, the smell of the sea, the hurrying, walking, running men, the ships loading and unloading, the cranes, the smell of tar and rope, all piled one on top of the other and dazed, dazzled, Yan took it all in.

He thought he had never been so happy in all his life.

From somewhere behind him, he heard the sound of church bells. He counted the chimes. One. Two. Three. Four. Five. With a start, he realised he would have to find the *Gar Leoch*, otherwise he would be late on board.

He was lucky. The *Gar Leoch* was tied up close by. She was a beautiful ship, lifting gently on the water. She had a chunky black body, with a red and white funnel.

By evening, the *Gar Leoch* had left Liverpool for Bangkok. On the first night, Yan couldn't sleep.

That was the first night but on the next night and every night thereafter, he slept like the dead.

Every day was a whirl of work.

'Scrub here. Scrub there. Paint here. Paint there. Clean this. Clean that.' All day and every day, Yan worked.

When his cabin mate said, 'Prepare yourself. We're going into the Bay of Biscay.' Yan simply smiled.

He didn't know what to do to prepare himself and anyway, he thought, what was there to prepare himself for?

They had been in the Bay two hours when the first storm blew up. He was on deck, scrubbing, beginning to feel as if he knew every inch of that deck, as well as every inch of brass rail.

One minute, the *Gar Leoch* was riding the waves nicely, the next, she wanted to turn over and sail upside down.

The sky turned black and the wind was so strong, the waves reared around the ship like mountains.

Yan was glad to go back to his cabin for a few hours sleep but when he woke, the storm was worse than ever and with a sinking heart, he realised he was on watch.

Struggling on to the deck, he was unprepared for the ferocity of the wind smashing into him as he came into the open. He didn't dare let go of one handhold before he found the next. The wind was determined to blow him into the boiling sea.

Once, Yan looked up and above him there was a solid wall of water with a curling white top. He thought of the Israelites walking through the Red Sea and wondered if they had been as scared as he was.

With a noise like thunder, the wave collapsed and sent the *Gar Leoch* soaring.

The ship soared and plunged, plunged and soared until Yan's head was spinning and he felt as sick as if he were on a roller coaster.

By the time he had reached the wheel house, dragged the door open and thrown himself into its warm lit safety, Yan had almost decided he would take a job on land.

Dawn was spectacular. A limpid gold sun crept over the horizon. The storm had gone as suddenly as it had arrived. Now, shoals of flying fish sparkled past the *Gar Leoch* and schools of porpoises played in the dark water.

By the time Yan's watch ended, he thought he might stay at sea.

After this, there was the Suez Canal where convoys of ships seemed to sail on sand. Wherever Yan looked, the desert stretched beyond his eyes' reach and the straight solid ribbon of water pushed its way through the sand, defeating one small part of the desert.

The sun baked and blistered the paintwork, bleached the decks until they were bone white and sent a thousand lights shooting off the brass and silver fittings.

Then, almost before Yan knew where he was, the ship was standing off the mouth of the Bangkok river. The Pilot came on board and guided the *Gar Leoch* up the stretch of water where the banks were lined with rough wooden jetties.

On the jetty alongside the *Gar Leoch*, Yan saw two small elephants.

'These are yours.' the officer on watch told him. 'You must look after them until we reach Hong Kong.'

All Yan's happiness drained away. Looking at the elephants, he felt like jumping ship. Vanishing, disappearing into the vast noisy world of Bangkok.

This was the first time he had ever seen an elephant and now there were two of them and he was to be their nursemaid.

They weren't baby elephants, either, he thought ruefully. They were teenage elephants and he could tell from the look in their eyes that neither of them wanted to be on the *Gar Leoch*.

The crane on board ship lifted the elephants onto the deck as if they were sticks of candy.

That was the end of all peace for Yan.

He called them Zoot and Soot and soon found out that Zoot and Soot never wanted to sleep. What they wanted was to play and to get out of their bamboo cages.

The elephants leant heavily against the bamboo bars, pushed them with their heads, curled their trunks around them and jostled until they were almost in danger of falling overboard.

And they ate!

Every day, Yan staggered along the deck with skyscrapers of bamboo shoots. The elephants ate them in a flash and looked for more.

Between looking after Zoot and Soot and doing his other duties, Yan lost track of time, until one morning, he looked at the calendar over his bunk and saw that the *Gar Leoch* was due to dock in Hong Kong on Advent Sunday.

Last Advent Sunday, he remembered, he had been walking in the hills. It was cold and snowy.

The heat of Bangkok was like a thick wet blanket, stifling everything it touched.

Two days before the *Gar Leoch* docked in Hong Kong, the elephants finally escaped.

Yan could hear them, trumpeting, stamping their feet, roaring their pleasure as they stampeded up and down the deck.

He ran after them, calling their names.

'Zoot. Soot. Come here' – but the elephants were having too much fun.

They were wildly excited, charging around like miniature canons. When they were quieter, Yan offered them bamboo shoots and they seized them in their trunks and flung them over their backs, trumpeting with joy.

Round and round and round the deck they ran until quite suddenly, they were tired and they stopped, allowing Yan to scratch their foreheads and lead them back into their cages.

'I don't know what was wrong with them,' he said.

'It's land.' the officer told him. 'They can smell it. It makes them crazy. They want to feel solid ground under their feet.'

The *Gar Leoch* docked in Hong Kong on the first day of December.

After a last banana, Zoot and Soot were hoisted off ship and Yan, almost as excited as they had been, made his way to the Sailor's Church.

It was packed to the rafters.

That year, he celebrated the birth of Christ with hundreds of other men from the sea, all of them singing and speaking a hundred different languages.

When it was all done and the last carol had been sung and the last prayer had been said, Yan went back aboard.

'Happy Christmas, Yan,' the officer shouted and later, in the purple midnight of Christmas Eve, Yan echoed him.

'Happy Christmas, world. Happy Christmas.'

Gwen Grant.

Feeding time

'Terry?' called Mrs Clark. There was no answer. She shook her head, wiped her hands on the towel beside the sink and went upstairs.

'Terry,' she said, addressing the dark lump in the middle of the rumpled bed, 'come on, it's nearly half-past ten.' The lump stirred.

'I'm tired.'

'Well, you should get to bed earlier instead of watching those stupid films. I don't think they're very suitable for a boy of your age anyway.' Terry rolled over and laughed.

'Well, you should stop me then, shouldn't you? Parents' responsibility and all that.'

'Don't be cheeky ... And get up at once. Aunt Dolly wants you to pop down and see her.'

'Oh Gawd! Do I have to?'

'I think it might be worth your while,' said Mrs Clark as she drew the curtains and threw open the window.

'Oh, ho! What does that mean?' asked Terry, squinting against the sudden light.

'Go and see,' said Mrs Clark and left the room.

'We'll only be gone a few days,' said Aunt Dolly, 'so the budgie won't be much bother. Just make sure he has some seed and water. But you'll need to clean Snowy out, otherwise he gets in a terrible mess.' Terry regarded the rabbit with some distaste. He thought he'd never seen such a stupid-looking creature. But then he thought of the crisp new five-pound note in his pocket.

'OK, Auntie, don't you worry. I'll keep 'em both in good nick.'

Next morning Terry was up early and round to Aunt Dolly's by 8.30. He filled the budgie's seed hopper and water bottle in no time at all; then he went to look at Snowy. He didn't seem too bad, but he still cleaned him out, just as Aunt Dolly had shown him, and made sure he had plenty of food. 'This is a doddle,' he thought.

The next morning he had promised to go to the precinct to meet Wayne and Johnnie, but he overslept again. When he did wake he could only find his old jeans, which looked ridiculous anyway, so what with being late and shouting at his mum about the jeans, he was in quite a temper when he left the house.

'Don't forget Aunt Dolly's!' shouted Mrs Clark after him.

'Oh blow!' said Terry. He did Snowy first this time. He didn't bother to clean out the hutch, but just threw some green leaves in and hurriedly latched the door and went towards the house. A small sound behind him made him turn. The door hadn't latched properly and there was Snowy, half out of the hutch, nose twitching in all directions. He ran back, but the rabbit was out, and lolloping away across the lawn. By the time he caught him Terry was really late, so he decided to skip the budgie. He'd given it plenty the day before, so it should be all right.

The next day Mrs Clark had real problems getting Terry out of bed, and it was midday before he got round to Aunt Dolly's. He could smell the rabbit hutch from the garden gate. 'Yuk,' he said and decided to do the budgie first. Both seed hopper and water bottle were empty. 'Stupid things,' thought Terry, 'they're not nearly big enough.' Then another thought struck him. He stared at the cage for a moment and then went to the kitchen cupboard. He came back with two cereal bowls, one of them brimming with water. He emptied the whole seed packet into the other and put them in the bottom of the cage. 'There,' he said, 'that should take care of you for a day or two.' The smell of the hutch hit him again as soon as he opened the back door. He decided to skip Snowy for that day.

The day Aunt Dolly was due to return Terry gritted his teeth and tackled the hutch. It was still rather smelly after his efforts, but he hoped it would clear by the time she arrived. He removed the cereal bowls from the budgie's cage and tried to clear up the seed which had gone all over the place. The budgie didn't seem to have touched the water, but when he filled the bottle it went to it straight away.

That evening Aunt Dolly came round. 'I just wanted to thank you for all your trouble, Terry.'

'That's OK, Auntie – any time.'

'You didn't notice anything odd about the budgie, did you?' Terry felt his stomach turn over. He thought his Mum was looking at him rather hard.

'Odd?' he asked.

'Oh, he just seemed a bit under the weather,' said Aunt Dolly, 'I'll have to get a tonic for him in the morning.'

'I think he may have missed you,' said Terry, very relieved. Aunt Dolly was very flattered.

Michael Proctor

A place called Goodwill

Kalyana Sundaram was just ten years old when he travelled thousands of miles from his home high in the Palni hills of Southern India to visit our school. I shall always remember him. Not just for his unusual name, thick black hair or permanent grin showing rows of sparkling white teeth. But for the cricket.

After Mr Foster had shown us slides of Goodwill village where he and Kalyana lived, everyone went out into the yard for a break. The boys desperately wanted the visitor to join their game of football but his quick glance at Mr Foster and a longer look down at his feet ended their hopes. There could be no football in those highly polished, brand new shoes! Instead he uttered one of his few words of English.

'Cricket?' he asked hopefully.

It wasn't cricket weather but someone fetched the playground stumps, a bat and tennis ball and the game began. Kalyana chose to bowl. Immediately he proceeded to knock the wickets over with remarkable ease. It was an unforgettable sight. Long fingers spun the ball with such startling effect that it developed a life of its own. Batsmen were mesmerised as they flailed around trying to make contact. Very soon the entire school had been dismissed. I bet he was chuckling all the way back to his distant home.

Yet less than thirty years ago Goodwill village did not exist, even in the dreams of its remarkable founder. John Foster, returning from a two-year teacher exchange in New Zealand, had decided to make it the journey of a lifetime.

In his words it turned out to be, 'a ticket to a much greater adventure'. After crossing Australia he sailed across the Indian Ocean to Sri Lanka and so to the subcontinent of India. Then followed a journey to Bombay, travelling for three and a half days at twenty five miles an hour on a crowded train with thirty coaches. At every stop the carriages were besieged by hordes of people. Some were selling produce. Most were ragged, barefoot, hungry, orphaned children begging pitifully.

At Adoni station John Foster bought two packets of biscuits. It was a transaction that changed his life. As he removed a wrapper he noticed a dozen outstretched hands reaching through the open carriage window towards him in supplication. He offered the biscuits through the window then opened the second packet and gave those away too. As the train drew away from the platform and he waved to the children he'd fed, their image became fixed in his mind. 'I'll come back one day to help children like you,' he promised.

Back in England he picked up the threads of his life, found a new teaching post, married and set up home. But the seeds of Goodwill had been sown on that platform in Adoni. In 1973 the Foster family sold up and travelled to Madurai province in Southern India. There he rented an apartment in the village of Thandigudi. Three times a day Mrs Foster served meals of rice to the hungry homeless children that queued at the door. It was not enough. John purchased three and a half acres of scrub land. Every morning at four o'clock he set off for his hillside patch of ground and single-handedly began to clear the dense undergrowth of the scrub jungle. For seven hours he worked, chopping, sawing, hacking and burning until the midday sun made it impossible to continue. Only then did he return to his house.

After several months, however, funds were desperately low. He had written 1,030 letters to friends all over Britain outlining his plans for a village to house destitute children, without receiving a single reply.

As he sat under a mango tree in the centre of the village one afternoon it seemed he must abandon his dream. Suddenly four ragged boys appeared before him. They had heard of the white man in Thandigudi who was building a house for orphans and had walked twenty miles to find shelter. Sadly John Foster couldn't help them. The house wasn't ready yet. So he gave them five rupees each for the fare back to their own village and the cost of a meal. But they didn't go. Instead they walked the two miles to the next village of Mangalamcombu and told the story to the head man. A few hours later a gang of volunteer workers presented themselves to John, freely offering their help.

Shortly afterwards more good news arrived. A letter from St Mark's C.E. School in Stockton containing £170. His first reply. The project was saved.

Buildings began to spring up and, as word spread, children arrived from all over the region. At Goodwill Village they found more than just a place to live. They found love, companionship and a sense of belonging. Everyone was their brother or sister.

Together they worked to make the homes comfortable. A well was sunk, a reservoir created, kitchens, a school, animal shelters, and even a theatre were built under John Foster's care and guidance. Today over 700 children are housed in seven homes spread throughout Southern India.

Occasionally John Foster returned to Britain reporting his progress to the hundreds of schools that support his work, and he usually took one of his young pupils with him. That was how I met Kalyana. I don't think he's made India's test team yet, but he has been to college and gained a degree and is back working in the village that rescued him from a life of poverty and hardship. A place called Goodwill.

Tom Quincey

The Tooth

The great white rock towered sixty feet above the sand below. Square topped and sheer it could be seen from all over the island.

People called it The Tooth.

And none knew it better than Koku.

Every day he would join the men-folk of his village to walk the few miles to the sea. But every day he was the last to arrive. Even the old men would pass him.

'Come on Koku,' they said kindly. 'You'll catch no fish again today.'

They meant no harm. It was their little joke. But the boy didn't laugh. By the time Koku reached the shore the canoes were already out of sight.

They would return at dusk. Then he would help to unload the catch, drag the boats back up the beach and stow them safely away for the night. That was his special job. He was always the last to leave, always the last to return to the village. Until then he joined the old men mending nets in the shade of the great rock. Sometimes he would listen to their tales of far off days, but when he grew bored with the chatter he would gaze out at the sea and wish for the thousandth time that he was riding the giant waves with his fathers and brothers.

Or he would stare up at The Tooth until he knew every inch of its shiny surface, every crack, every crevice. Countless times Koku had climbed to the very top, stood on its flat peak and waved to his friends in the fishing boats or his mother and sisters in the village. But only in his dreams. Time dragged by that morning. It seemed like an eternity before dozens of tiny specks appeared on the horizon. The canoes were returning, carried ashore on the incoming tide, the freshening wind speeding their passage.

It had been a good catch. The nets were heavy with glistening silver fish.

His brothers were in playful mood.

'And what have you caught today Koku?' one asked as they came ashore.

'Maybe he's caught a cold,' replied another.

'Or a crab in those nets he's been mending.'

Their father frowned.

'Leave him alone,' he said sternly. 'Don't tease....'

Laughing, the brothers turned away and ran back down to the water to empty the boats.

It was a long time before Koku could begin his final task. Alone on the beach he struggled to upturn the canoes and stack them in the shelter of The Tooth.

The wind was strengthening and becoming chill. Clouds raced each other across the darkening sky. A storm was approaching. Koku hated storms. Usually they would pass harmlessly across the island barely pausing to dampen the villagers below.

But occasionally they were in determined mood like gatecrashers at a party wreaking havoc and upset before moving on. Koku grimaced at the thought. Oh yes, Koku hated storms. He looked seaward again. There was no horizon anymore. Clouds and waves had merged into a huge grey wall moving slowly towards the shore.

His job done, Koku turned his back and hurried towards the path through the sand dunes. For a brief moment the air became still. The roar of wind and waves died down. There was silence. The boy sensed that something was wrong. He remembered the story the old men told of a terrible night before his grandfather was born. A night when the angry sea swallowed up the island, leaving only the great rock and the tallest trees standing above the waves.

Koku looked back once more. Slowly, but surely, the wall of water was coming closer. Again he felt the fierce wind beat in his face. Suddenly he knew what he must do. Reaching forward he rummaged amongst the pebbles at the foot of The Tooth. Water was already beginning to trickle between his fingers as he searched. At last he was satisfied. He tucked his find safely inside his belt and stared up at the huge rock. The time for dreaming was over. Now he really had to climb.

He'd planned the path so many times before. But he could never have imagined the strength of the wind, or the ache in his shoulders as he pulled himself upwards carefully seeking out every handhold. He'd known pain before. Real pain. For hours he had lain crushed beneath the great tree that had crashed down on his family's hut while the men struggled to lift it from his legs. Now those legs were wasted. Useless. No fishing for him. He was fit only to mend nets and stack canoes with the old ones. Oh yes, he hated storms.

But this one wouldn't win. Koku had decided.

His arms were strong. He would reach the top and...

The sound of water interrupted his thoughts. Glancing down he could see huge waves beating against the rock, creeping ever higher up the beach.

Locking his fingers inside a tiny crevice he heaved his heavy legs higher up the rock face. He must reach the top and warn the village. Let them know of the danger. Give them time to reach safety.

But it was hard. The rock was greasy from the driving rain and his legs were a dead weight.

Once more he heard his brothers' mocking words – 'What did you catch today Koku, a cold?' – as he pulled himself nearer to The Tooth's flat summit. The beach was already submerged. Water was climbing the dunes. Soon it would find the path to the village. One last heave took Koku to the top. There was barely time to pause for breath. Then the boy reached inside his belt, took the huge conch shell and blew hard and long. A tuneless wail echoed around the rock.

From his perch high on the peak Koku could see tiny figures running from their huts and staring seawards. He blew into the shell once more and waved in desperation. They understood. In minutes the clearing was filled with people clutching bundles, carrying babies. Soon they would reach the safety of the huts built high in the treetops.

His work done, Koku lay exhausted on the flat rock top. By morning the unwelcome visitor would have left the island. Slowly the waters would recede and he would be able to climb down the rock. Once more he would help the old men mend nets and stack canoes when the boats returned from the sea laden with fish.

And Koku knew that no-one would laugh at him. Ever again.

Charles Marlow

The villagers of Eyam

When our story begins, the village of Eyam was unknown and even more isolated than it is now. But the villagers, three hundred and fifty of them, miners, weavers and their families, liked it that way.

They had heard terrible tales of big cities, particularly London where now a great plague had taken hold. People were dying in their thousands in great misery and pain. Whole families were being wiped out.

Well, at least that can't happen here, the villagers thought. But they were wrong.

Just past the church in Eyam is a small row of cottages, one of which is called 'Plague Cottage'. Of course, it wasn't called that in August 1665, when a horse and cart tumbled up the street and stopped outside it....

The carter jumped down.

'Mrs Cooper?' he bellowed. 'Mrs Cooper at home?'

'Aye, man,' said Mrs Cooper, coming out. 'What have you got now? Summat for me?'

'For your lodger. This box here labelled "Mr Viccars, tailor, Eyam." It's heavy, I'll tell you that.'

'It's full of cloth from London, that's why. Mr Viccars has been on the look-out for it this past month. You've taken your time.'

'Ere, it only came off the stage coach this morning!'

'Aye, well, I'll get my lads to give you a hand. Edward? Jonathan?'

Mr Viccars was delighted with the cloth. 'Some good stuff here, Mrs Cooper. Well worth the wait. Here, feel this. How about a new dress?'

Mrs Cooper ran rough hands over it.

'Too fine for the likes of me. Maybe her Ladyship – '

'That's what I'm hoping.'

'It needs a good shake before her Ladyship sees it – get the fleas out! And it's damp and creased. Let me spread it out in your workroom. It'll be aired enough ready for you to take in the morning.'

But by morning, Mr Viccars was overcome with a fit of shivering and fever. The pain came towards the evening and no-one got to sleep that night because of him crying out. Next day he was worse. Five days after the cloth was delivered he was dead. That couldn't be... no, surely not?

Then Mrs Cooper's sons, Edward and Jonathan, took ill....

Their names can be found, and Mr Viccars', heading the list in a book in the vicarage next to the other side of the church. The book, which was made later from the funeral lists, is called the Plague Register – for plague, the terrified villagers now had to admit, as the deaths multiplied, was what had come to Eyam.

Not surprisingly, at first some of them fled. The new vicar, William Mompesson, and his wife, Catherine, sent their two children off to friends. But, they decided, they couldn't desert the village at this time when they were needed most. The people were horribly afraid. And the funeral bell never seemed to be silent. More and more people decided to leave. Then they thought: Where shall we go? We may be carrying the plague to our friends, relations in other villages and cities. It could spread all over the country, and beyond. They turned to Mr Mompesson. What should they do?

Imagine those pews full of frightened villagers. From the pulpit, their vicar delivered his urgent message:

'And so, my dear friends, both I and your former minister here, Mr Stanley, have talked and prayed long together and now we feel we must put to you what we feel God is asking of us: it is that, for the sake of our neighbouring villages and beyond, we should not leave Eyam. We should stay together and keep this terrible plague within the confines of our village. It will be an awesome decision to make. It will need bravery and courage. Will you accept that this is what we should do?'

The villagers walked slowly from the church with their heads bowed. For they had made the decision. They had said yes: they would stay, they would fight the plague by keeping it locked in their own village.

Mr Mompesson pulled the door shut behind him and then locked it. From then on, they had also decided, they would no longer meet in enclosed places where the risk of spreading infection would be greater. Across the road, beyond the houses, was a field with a cleft in it, like a miniature valley. It was called the Delph. And here the villagers had their services and meetings. Standing in worried, isolated groups, they heard, as the weeks passed, the names of the dead and dying as the plague took its toll. 'My dear, dear friends,' Mr Mompesson would shout to them, 'since we last met we have lost...' and then would come the names, people who perhaps had been standing there last week: 'William Hawksworth, Thomas Kemp, Francis and Mary and Michael Booking, Mary Whitney....' But then his own dear wife, Catherine, fell ill. He prayed that the contagion had not reached her. But soon, a very sad letter was to reach their children, still away with friends.

As the months passed, the villagers realised the plague would soon have been with them for a year. How much longer? O Lord, how much longer?

On the outskirts of the village there was a boundary stone. It was here that villagers would leave money and step well back. Then outside traders would fearfully approach, leaving bread, meat, vegetables.

'How many gone since June?'

'Fifty-nine.'

'God have mercy on you!'

By September, the numbers of deaths had at last begun to decrease. The figures were watched with increasing hope: October, November, fewer deaths. Then in December, Mr Mompesson's words were carried by the blustering wind to the pitifully small number of villagers gathered in the Delph:

'My people, my dear people. It is now a month since, on November the first, our dear friend Abraham Martin died. Since then there have been no more deaths. I believe... yes, I believe that this pestilence has passed from us. Oh, my dear friends, we are so few in number now. Since the plague came, two hundred and sixty of us have died; only ninety remain. We cannot rejoice – how can we with the memory of so many loved ones gone from us? We can but be grateful that we have been spared, and that we have done what we set out to do: save others from what we have suffered. Let us open up our church once again and enter its gate with praise and thanksgiving....'

And now if you come on the last Sunday in August you'll find people gathered in the Delph. They come from miles around and further, to remember and give thanks for those villagers who, in the midst of misery, pain and death, thought of the others they could save from it.

Arthur Scholey

An honest thief

Every village has a 'bad man' of its own, and St Victoria Village was no exception. It had Mr Spencer. Mr Spencer was a real 'bad man', and not even Big Joe would venture to cross his path.

Mr Spencer didn't ever go out of his way to interfere with anybody, but everybody knew what happened to anybody who was foolish enough to interfere with Mr Spencer. Mr Spencer had a reputation.

Now, at the time I am speaking of, every morning when Mr Spencer got up, he made the sign of the cross, went and cleaned his teeth, and then left the house and went into the open yard to look at his banana tree. He had a lovely banana tree. Its trunk was beautiful and long and graceful, the leaves wide and shiny, and, in the morning, with the dew-drops glinting silvery on them, it seemed like something to worship – at least Mr Spencer thought so.

Mr Spencer's wife used to say to him, 'Eh, but Selwyn, you like you bewitch or something. Every morning as God send I see you out there looking up in that banana tree. What happen? Don't tell me you starting to go dotish.'

But Mr Spencer would just grunt in reply.

The banana tree thrived under Mr Spencer's care. Its bunch of bananas grew and grew, and became bigger and lovelier every day. Mr Spencer said: 'They kin win first prize at any agricultural exhibition, you know, Ellie.'

'Yes, Selwyn,' she said.

And now, every morning Mr Spencer would jump out of bed the moment he woke and run outside to look at his banana tree. He would feel the bunch of bananas and murmur, 'Yes, they really coming good. I going give them a few more days.' And he would say this every day.

The lovelier the bananas grew, the more Mrs Spencer heard of them, all through the day. Mr Spencer would get up from his breakfast and say: 'I wonder if that tree all right! Ellie, you think so? Look, you better go and give it little water with the hose.' Or, he would wake up in the middle of the night, and rouse his wife and say, 'Hey, but Ellie, I wonder if the night temperature ain't too cold for the tree! I'd best had warm some water and put it to the roots ... along with some manure.

One morning Mr Spencer came in from the yard and said as usual, 'Ellie girl, them bananas real lovely now. I think I going pick them in couple days' time.'

'Always 'couple days',' she said, peeved. 'Man, why you don't pick them now quick before you lose them or something? You ain't even got no paling round the yard. Suppose somebody come in here one o' these nights and t'ief them?'

'T'ief which?' Mr Spencer said. 'T'ief which? T'ief which?'

The truth was, nobody in the village would have dared to steal Mr Spencer's bananas, for, as I have mentioned, he was a 'bad man'.

Then, one day, another 'bad man' came to live in the village. He was the biggest and toughest man anybody had ever seen. He had long hairy arms and a big square head and a wide mouth and his name was Bulldog.

Everybody said, 'One o' these days Bulldog and Mr Spencer going

clash. Two bad men can't live in the same village.' And they told Mr Spencer, 'Bulldog will beat you!'

'Beat who? Beat who? Beat who?' Mr Spencer said. He always repeated everything three times when he was indignant.

And Bulldog said: 'Who this Spencer is? Show him to me.'

So one evening they took Bulldog out by Mr Spencer's, and he came up where Mr Spencer was watering his tree and said: 'You is this Mr Spencer?'

'How that get your business?' Mr Spencer asked.

'Well, this is how. If you is this Spencer man, I kin beat you.' Bulldog always came straight to the point.

'Who say so? Who say so? Who say so?'

'I say so.'

Mr Spencer looked Bulldog up and down and said: 'Well, I ain't denying you might stand up to me for a few minutes.' He paused for a moment, and then said: 'But I bet you ain't got a banana tree like mine.'

He had Bulldog there. It was true that Bulldog had a banana tree, and, seen alone, it was a very creditable banana tree. But beside Mr Spencer's it was a little warped relic of a banana tree.

Bulldog said: 'Man, you got me there fir truth.'

'That ain't nothing,' Mr Spencer said. 'Look up there at them bananas.'

Bulldog looked. His eyes and mouth opened wide. He rubbed his eyes. He asked: 'Wait – them is real bananas?'

'Um-hum,' Mr Spencer replied modestly. 'Of course they still a bit young, so if they seem a little small ...'

'Small!' Bulldog said. 'Man, them is the biggest bananas I ever see in my whole life. Lemme taste one.'

'One o' which? One o' which? One o' which?'

Mr Spencer always repeated everything three times when he was indignant. 'Now, get out o' my yard!'

Bulldog left. But he vowed to taste one of Mr Spencer's bananas if it was the last thing he ever did.

Mrs Spencer told her husband: 'Don't go and bring yourself in any trouble with that jail-bird. Give he a banana and settle it.'

Mr Spencer said. 'If he want trouble, he come to the right place. Lemme ketch him' round that banana tree. I waiting for he.'

'C'dear, pick the bananas

and eat them all quick 'fore he come back and t'ief them.'

'No,' Mr Spencer said. 'I waiting for he. I waiting. Let him come and touch one – just one, and see what he get.'

A few days passed. Bulldog had tried to forget Mr Spencer's bananas, but he couldn't put them out of his mind. He did everything he could to rid his thoughts of that big beautiful bunch of bananas which had tempted him that day in Mr Spencer's yard.

And then he began to dream about them. He talked about them in his sleep. He began to lose weight. And every day when he passed by Mr Spencer's land, he would see Mr Spencer watering the banana tree, and manuring it, or just looking at it, and the bananas would seem to wink at Bulldog and challenge him to come and touch one of them.

One morning Bulldog woke up and said: 'I can't stand it no longer. I got to have one o' Spencer's bananas today by the hook or by the crook. I will go and ax him right now.' He got up and went to Mr Spencer.

Mr Spencer was in the yard feeling the bananas. He was saying to himself: 'Boy, these looking real good. I going to pick them tomorrow.'

Bulldog stood up at the edge of Mr Spencer's land; he didn't want to offend him by trespassing. He called out: 'Mr Spencer, please, give me one of your bananas.'

Mr Spencer turned round and saw him. He said: 'Look, get out o' my sight before I go and do something ignorant.'

And Bulldog said: 'This is you last chance. If I don't get a banana now, you losing the whole bunch, you hear?'

'But look at ... But look at ... But look at ...' Mr Spencer was so mad he could scarcely talk.

Now Bulldog was a conscientious thief. He had certain moral scruples. He liked to give his victims a fifty-fifty chance. He said: 'I going t'ief you bananas tonight, Spencer. Don't say I ain't tell you.'

'You's a idiot?' Mr Spencer called back. 'Why you don't come? I got a rifle and I will clap a shot in the seat o' you pants, so help me.'

'Anyhow, I going t'ief you bananas,' Bulldog said. 'I can't resist it no more.'

'Come as soon as you ready, but anything you get you kin tek.'

'That is okay,' Bulldog said. 'I tekking all o' them.'

Mr Spencer pointed to a sign under the banana tree. It read: TRESSPASSERS WILL BE PERSECUTED.

'And for you, persecuting mean shooting.'

Bulldog said nothing more but went home.

A little later in the day, a little boy brought a message on a piece of note-paper to Mr Spencer. It read, 'I will thief your bananas between 6 o'clock tonite and 2 o'clock tomorra morning.' Mr Spencer went inside and cleaned his gun.

Mrs Spencer said, 'But look how two big men going kill theyself over a bunch o' bananas! Why you don't go and pick them bananas *now* and mek sure he can't get them.'

'Woman,' Mr Spencer replied, 'this is a matter of principle. I refuse to tek the easy way out. Bulldog is a blasted robber and he must be stopped, and I, Adolphus Selwyn McKenzie Hezekiah Spencer, is the onliest man to do it. Now, you go and boil some black coffee for me. I will have to drink it and keep awake tonight if I is to stand up for law and order.'

At six o'clock Mr Spencer sat down at his backdoor with his rifle propped upon the step and trained on the banana tree. He kept his eyes fixed there for the slightest sign of movement, and didn't even blink. It was a lovely moonlight night. 'If he think I mekking sport, let him come, let him come, let him come.'

Seven eight, nine, ten, eleven, twelve o'clock. And no sign of Bulldog. And Mr Spencer hadn't taken his eyes off the banana tree once. In the moonlight the tree stood there lovely and still, and the bananas glistened. Mr Spencer said, 'They real good now. I going pick them tomorrow without fail.'

Mrs Spencer said: 'Look, Selwyn, come lewwe go to bed. The man ain't a fool. He ain't coming.'

'Ain't two o'clock yet,' Mr Spencer said.

And all the time Mrs Spencer kept him supplied with bread and black coffee. He took his food with one hand and disposed of it without ever taking his eyes off the tree. The other hand he kept on the gun, one finger on the trigger. He was determined not to take his eyes off that tree.

One o'clock. No Bulldog.

Half past one. No Bulldog.

Quarter to two. No Bulldog.

Mrs Spencer said: 'The man ain't coming. Lewwe go to bed. Is a quarter to two now.'

'We may as well wait till two and done now,' Mr Spencer said.

Ten to two. No Bulldog.

'This is a waste o' good time.' Mr Spencer said.

Five to two.

At one minute to two, Mr Spencer looked at his wristwatch to make sure and turned his head and said to his wife, 'But look how this dam vagabond make we waste we good time.'

Then he looked back at the banana tree. He stared. His mouth opened wide. The banana tree stood there empty, and the only indication that it had once proudly displayed its prize bunch of bananas was the little stream of juice that was dribbling down from the bare, broken stem.

In that one moment, in a twinkling of his eye, everything that Mr Spencer had treasured and cared about so much, had simply vanished.

Traditional West Indian tale adapted by Timothy Callender

The Atlantic Star

When I was little, Saturday was always Grandad's day. Mum or Dad used to drop me off in the morning, then pick me up again at tea time. It was the same every week. We played dominoes or cards in the living room on a little table in front of the fire. But he never let me win.

'The day you beat me,' he used to say, 'You'll do it fair and square.'

I didn't mind. He always reached down a big tin of toffees from the cupboard and we munched our way through hundreds while we played. At least I did. Grandad took ages to eat just one.

'It's me teeth,' he complained.

When I laughed he said, 'You wait boy. Your turn'll come. And the way you're chomping, it won't be long.'

Afterwards I'd rummage through drawers while he messed about in the kitchen. Old photographs, postcards and mementoes but best of all, his medals. I'd pin them on and march up and down. Dinner was always the same. Mashed potatoes, fried bacon and tomatoes, Jam pudding and custard.

'That's the stuff to give the troops,' he'd say. I loved it.

On winter afternoons we wrapped up warm and went to the park. Sometimes there was ice to break on the boating lake. In summer I'd sail my yacht, throw a ball, swing on the swings and when Grandad was tired, sit by the bowling green and eat ice cream. When I asked him why he didn't play bowls he'd say, 'Old man's game boy. Look at 'em. Rolling the ball, hands on hip, standing and watching, prancing up and down. How can anyone get excited about that?'

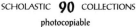

'Have you ever had a go?'

'Don't need to,' he said dismissively, 'old man's game.' And he turned back to his ice cream. That was far more interesting than bowls. First he licked all the ice cream from the top, then broke the end off the cornet and sucked the rest through the hole in the bottom.

'Is it because of your teeth Grandad?' I asked. He laughed.

'Course not. Tastes better this way!'

So I did the same.

One afternoon just before mum came to collect me, Grandad said, 'It's time to give you this.' He'd fetched his medals from the drawer in the front room. Reaching over he pinned one on my chest. Red and blue ribbon, bronze five-pointed medallion. The Atlantic Star. My favourite.

He saluted and smiled.

'There you are boy, you're in the navy now.'

And he let me keep it.

The next Saturday my best friend Simon asked me to go ice skating with him and his dad.

'You must tell Grandad,' mum said. 'He'll have your dinner ready you know.'

So I rang him.

'OK boy,' he said. 'Falling on your backside is more exciting than watching the old 'uns bowling isn't it? I don't blame you. See you next Saturday.'

But I didn't. I always seemed to find something else to do. Weekends were too short.

Sometimes I went to Grandad's on Sundays but it wasn't the same anymore. Mum and Dad and Paula my sister went as well.

'Have you given me the sack?' Grandad asked one day.

'Course not,' I replied. My voice was hoarse and my face was burning. I was embarrassed and angry at the same time. Perhaps that's why I swapped the medal.

Alan Coles had a marvellous conker. Big, bright and a rich chestnut red, it was king of the playground. He hardly seemed to draw back the string before shells shattered into hundreds of tiny pieces. It was a real champion. A forty-fiver. And I envied him.

'What do you want for your conker?' I asked at morning break.

'What have you got?'

I thought hard.

'A packet of felt tips.'

'You must be joking!' he sneered. 'Felt pens? For a forty-fiver? No way!'

I tried again.

'Fifty football stickers.'

'Rubbish,' he shouted, 'you can keep your stickers.'

And you can keep your conker, I thought. But then I remembered the medal.

'The Atlantic Star,' I said.

'What's that?'

'It's in my desk. I'll show it to you after play.'

We did the deal in Maths. I hid the medal under my book and passed it across the table. He lifted the cover, looked at the star, raised his eyebrows and nodded. Then he slipped the medal into his pocket, put the book on top of the conker and slid it back. I held the shiny ball in my palm. I could feel its warmth spreading through my fingers like a vital force. A strange power. I couldn't wait for lunch-time to get into the yard and try it out. But I never got the chance. Alan was waiting for me in the cloakroom.

'I've changed my mind,' he said.

'You can't. It's not fair. A swap's a swap.'

'Not when I'm bigger than you its not. Here's your medal. Give me my conker back. Or else!'

So I did.

And I wasn't half glad.

We'd only just got into the playground when Jamie Kite's three-er cracked the champion. First hit. His second shot snagged the string but the third shattered Alan's conker to smithereens.

When I got home that evening I knew something was wrong. Dad was there much earlier than usual.

'OK son,' he said quietly. 'Can you be brave?'

I nodded. I thought I could.

'Grandad's been rushed into hospital. He's very poorly.'

Remembering the ice-cream cornets, breaking ice on the pond and the domino games I swallowed hard to keep away the tears.

'He's a good age Steven,' Dad said.

'But not old enough for bowls,' I replied, and closed my hand tightly around the cold metal star in my pocket.

Ian Addis

A special friend

Have you got a special friend? Someone to whom you can tell all your innermost secrets? You're lucky if you have. Such people are rare. That is why Anne was pleased with her birthday present. So pleased that she wrote, *'I hope I shall be able to confide in you completely, as I have never been able to do in anyone before, and I hope that you will be a great support and comfort to me.'*

So what do you think the present was?

It was a book. A book with stiff covers and lots of empty pages. Plenty of room to write her thoughts.

Her first entry ends: *'Bye-bye, we're going to be great pals.'*

And she named her special friend Kitty.

So began an incredible story of courage, love and eventual betrayal. The early pages are full of typical light hearted comments about family, school and friends. Anne was very much an ordinary schoolgirl, labelled a chatterer by her maths teacher. But the times were far from normal. This was Amsterdam in June 1942. Anne's parents were Otto and Edith Frank. They emigrated from Germany in 1933, the year that Adolf Hitler became Chancellor.

Now Holland, like most of Western Europe, was under German occupation. Anne and her sister Margot were treated like criminals. They were required to wear a huge, yellow six-pointed star on their clothing. They were forbidden to do those ordinary things we take for granted: travel by train, visit a cinema, swimming baths or tennis court, ride a bicycle or sit in the garden after eight o'clock in the evening. Their crime? They were Jewish. Much worse was to come. Less than a month after Anne's thirteenth birthday, Mr Frank received a call-up notice from the Gestapo, the German secret police. Anne understood what this meant. Her father must join the thousands of Jews and 'inferiors' deported to concentration camps. There he would be forced to work in a slave labour gang until starvation or execution claimed his life. Such treatment was not confined to men. No-one was spared; the whole family was at risk. So they decided to go into hiding.

Into hiding, Anne wrote. *Where would we go, to a town or the country, in a house or a cottage, when, how, where...?*

There was only time to pack a few precious belongings – hair curlers, school books and her beloved diary.

The chosen place was the two upper back floors above the office building where her father had worked. Mr Frank had spent months preparing the hideaway and now it was ready. Anne called it the 'Secret Annexe', its entry hidden behind filing cabinets and a revolving cupboard. Here the family were to eat, sleep, and fill every minute of every day until the war was won and they could emerge in safety. Or until they were found.

Saturday, 11th July 1942. Dear Kitty,
I can't tell you how oppressive it is never to be able to go outdoors, also I'm scared to death we shall be discovered and shot...

The fear was very real. Even the slightest noise, a cough, a dripping tap, a dropped book could betray their position to the people working in the building downstairs.

When a plumber came to move water pipes in the office below, the family were unable to use the toilet or speak or move for the entire day.

Tension increased with the arrival of other Jewish families to share their hiding place. You can imagine what it was like if you've ever been cooped up with your brother or sister on a wet day in the holidays with nowhere to go and nothing much to do.

Saturday, 27th September 1942. Dear Kitty,
Just had a big bust up with Mummy for the umpteenth time... and Margot and I don't hit it off any too well either.

There were few contacts with the outside world. Food and supplies had to be carried in by Dutch friends who risked their own lives. One special helper was Miep Van Santen who worked in the office downstairs. She also brought frightening news of the fate of other Jewish families, torn apart, deprived of possessions and carted off to face certain death in the labour camps. Little wonder that Anne occasionally gave vent to feelings of despair.

Wednesday, 3rd May 1944
What, oh what is the use of war? Why can't people live peaceably together? Why all this destruction?... Oh why are people so crazy?

Yet throughout the long hours of silence and inactivity Anne never gave up hope. She wrote about her dreams for the future, expressing her joy and gratitude for her safety and good health and the beauty of the world.

Their tiny radio set brought news of D-Day and the successful Allied invasion. Hopes were raised. Holland would soon be free again. Anne looked forward to leaving her prison of safety and hunger and returning to school. But it was not to be.

On August 4th, 1944 armed secret police raided the office and discovered the hiding place. The family had been betrayed. Everyone was arrested, packed in cattle trucks and transported to extermination centres in German occupied Poland. Mrs Frank perished in Auschwitz. Anne and her sister Margot died in the infamous concentration camp at Belsen in February 1945.

The Secret Annexe had been plundered during the raid. Everything was removed except a pile of newspapers and a couple of notebooks, which were given by an office cleaner to Miep Van Santen who kept them hidden until the war had ended. They contained Anne's diaries.

Mr Frank, incredibly, survived the death camp, and in 1947 published his daughter's story for the world to read. One of Anne's final entries reads:

Dear Kitty,
..... I want to go on living even after my death.

Her special friend ensures that she does.

Charles Marlow

The Real Wonder (or The boy who could flick peas into a milk bottle)

There once was a boy called Arthur (though his mother called him Arty). When he was two years old, to keep him quiet, his mother put a bowl of dried peas on the carpet and said, 'Arty dear, fill this milk bottle with peas, one pea at a time.' And when he had filled the bottle, she gave him a sweet. Then he emptied the peas back into the bowl and started all over again – always one pea at a time.

And Arty's mother said to *her* mother, 'Isn't our Arty clever!' And Arty's grandma said, 'Bless his little heart, he's a Wonder. He's a Real Wonder!'

'He's wasting his time' his grandad said. (But no-one ever listened to *him*.)

And, every day, even Sundays, Arty filled milk bottles with dried peas – always one at a time.

Then one day when he was three, he balanced a pea on his first finger and flicked it into the air with his thumb and it fell into the milk bottle. And soon he could flick a pea into a bottle from three centimetres away. Then six centimetres away. Then twelve centimetres away. Then the length of a ruler away.

His mother said, 'Just look at him. Our Arty gets cleverer every day!'

And his grandma said, 'Yes, bless his little heart, he's a Wonder, a Real Wonder. And look, Arty I've brought you this big bag of sweeties.'

'They'll rot his teeth' his grandad said. (But no-one heard him.)

When Arty started school he didn't like it. The teacher wouldn't let him flick peas into milk bottles and she didn't give him sweets nor tell him he was a Real Wonder or even an Ordinary Wonder. So Arty said he had stomach-ache and his mother kept him at home where he could flick peas into milk bottles all day long.

And his grandma said, 'Isn't he a Wonder! If only the King could see him at it!' But his grandad who had played for Manchester United said, 'I wish he'd play football,' and gave him one for his birthday. But Arty said, 'A football is too heavy for me to flick with my thumb and it's too big to drop into a milk bottle top. On my next birthday, buy me a big bag of dried peas.'

By the time he was ten he could flick peas from one end of the sitting-room to the other and they *always* dropped into the milk bottle. And his mother said, 'If our Arty keeps this up, someday he will throw darts so they always stick in the dart board where he wants them to stick. Or he will knock snooker balls into the pockets he wants them to drop into. Or he will hit little golf balls so they always fall into the little holes he wants them to fall into. Then he will be on TV and will win thousands and thousands of pounds.'

('And he'll never have done a proper day's work in his life,' humphed his grandad, but no-one was listening to *him*.)

Then, as it happened, the King sent a message to every town and village saying, 'THE NEXT TIME I COME I SHALL EXPECT TO BE SHOWN THE MOST WONDERFUL THING YOU HAVE. THERE WILL BE PRIZES.'

At one place they showed him a cat with two tails and the King gave them one hundred tins of gold-plated Katty-Kit. (The tins were gold-plated not the Katty-Kit). At another place they showed him a motor car that ran on tap water and he gave them a gold-plated hose-pipe. At another place he was shown a girl who could work out in her head what 2,365 add 6,089 take away 2,785 multiplied by 187 and divided by 99 came to. And he gave her a gold-plated calculator and said, 'This will stop you wearing out your brain, dear.'

When he got to Arty's town they showed him Arty. 'Your Majesty,' they said, 'This little lad can kneel at one side of the road and flick peas into a milk bottle on the other side of the road. Even when there's a wind blowing.'

(And Arty's grandma shouted, 'Bless his little heart, he's World Famous round here! Everybody except his grandad knows he's a Real Wonder.')

So the King called out, 'LET HIM BEGIN.'

And Arty got down on one knee and flicked pea after pea across the road. And not one missed the bottle top.

'ARISE ARTY,' the King commanded, 'AND APPROACH. NOW CLOSE YOUR EYES AND HOLD OUT YOUR HAND FOR YOUR PRIZE. RIGHT! NOW YOU CAN LOOK AND SEE WHAT I'VE GIVEN YOU.'

And it was one dried pea.

'I SHALL NOW GIVE YOU A TEST,' the King said.

'FIRST YOUR TIMES TABLES. WHAT ARE EIGHT SEVENS?'

'Fifteen,' said Arty.

'WRONG. NOW SPELLING. SPELL PEA.'

'P-e-e,' answered Arty.

'WRONG. THAT IS ANOTHER KIND OF PEA. WHO WAS THE FIRST MAN?'

'Grandad,' said Arty.

'Just as I thought,' the King said. 'You have only learned to flick peas into milk bottles by neglecting your education. You are not at all wonderful. IN FACT YOU ARE AWFUL. Is there a salt mine near here? There is! Oh good! See that this idle fellow goes down the salt mine and digs salt. And he is only to be allowed to come up for air on one day a year. On Christmas Day. And his Christmas Dinner must be a basin of mushy peas.'

Then Arty and his mother and his grandma fell upon their knees and sobbed, 'Oh mercy, your Majesty.'

'Well alright,' the King said. 'But first he must push that pea with his nose the length of a football pitch. And from now on he must only do useful things like washing up and learning his tables.

('And playing football!' cried his grandad.)

'Yes,' said the King. 'And playing football. But mind you, no fouls.'

And from that time on, Arthur did only useful things.

And, when he left school, he got a steady job – as a milkman.

J. L. Carr

It's the little things that matter

When he was a boy, just a bit younger than you, your Great Grandad lived up in Scotland. He had four brothers and four sisters and was the youngest in the family. They didn't have very much money in those days; everyone went off to work as soon as they were old enough.

The family lived near the River Tay and they could see the Tay Bridge from their house. Your Great Grandad was able to watch them building it when he was little. It took six years to build, and at that time, was the longest bridge in the world – nearly two miles long. In those Victorian times, it had been a very difficult bridge to build: several men lost their lives in accidents.

Great Grandad loved watching the trains that crossed over the River Tay on the bridge. He was fascinated by the noise and the thick plumes of smoke. Whenever the signal showed a train was approaching, he would hurry to his favourite viewing spot.

Sometimes, he would stand underneath the huge metal supports of the bridge and feel the vibrations caused by the train.

It was during one of these occasions that he found the first nut and bolt.

At breakfast the next morning, when they were all tucking into their salty porridge, Great Grandad put the nut and bolt on the table in front of his parents.

He was told that nuts and bolts were used to fix pieces of metal together. They became his treasures. He thought that a nut was a strange name for a small metal object: he enjoyed looking through the hole in the centre. He wondered how it was made. He fixed the nut and bolt tightly together and put them in his pocket.

The train to Dundee would be coming over the bridge soon. He ran off to watch it. The train was not signalled, so he decided to sit on a stone by the bridge and wait. His hand leant on something hard. He looked down – another bolt. He looked closer. There were bolts everywhere. Before the bell rang in the nearby signal box to herald the approach of a train, he had found nearly forty bolts.

He watched the train from beneath the bridge. He enjoyed hunting for bolts. He spent most of the day searching. He filled three trouser pockets, two jacket pockets and his cap full of nuts and bolts.

You can imagine him staggering home through long grass, up steep banks, over stony tracks clutching at his cap and worrying because the overloaded pockets made him feel that his trousers were falling off. He was only a little lad.

'Mother! Mother!' he shouted. He hurtled into the kitchen nearly scattering his capful of bolts all over the floor.

When the rest of the family returned from work, there were one hundred and seventy six bolts in line by the fireplace. They decided that they had been left behind by the bridge builders.

Great Grandad now spent every day collecting bolts from beneath the Tay Bridge. Every available space at home was used for rows and rows of bolts.

One Sunday afternoon in November, he took the whole family to see where he hunted. His parents were amazed: the area was peppered with them. They walked along to the signal box to tell the railwaymen what they had found.

Great Grandad shouted out. 'Your bridge is falling to pieces. I think you ought to mend it!'

The railwaymen were not at all concerned: 'We've got the best and longest bridge in the world here. I don't think we need to worry about these little bolts.'

Even when the rest of the family explained that there were even more bolts beneath the bridge, no-one would take any action. Great Great Grandfather wrote letters to Dundee about the bridge, but his letters were ignored.

On Sunday 28th December 1879, the same two men were in the signal box when the train to Dundee was signalled, just after seven o'clock. At the regulation speed of 3mph, the train moved slowly across the bridge. A violent gale howled as the two men watched the lights on the rear of the train. Suddenly they could no longer see them. They rushed out of the signal box onto the railway line. The tracks seemed to be swaying. They didn't go far, for there, in the moonlight, they could see that the centre of the bridge had disappeared and so had the train, its coaches, and seventy five passengers.

This was a disaster that could have been averted. Those bolts had been shaken loose by the vibration of the trains.

Great Grandad said little things always matter. He was right.

Sue Spooner

Today we're going to do poetry

Have you noticed how, whenever it's very foggy or very frosty or very windy your teacher will announce.

'Today we're going to do poetry.'

There are groans around the room. It means you have to put on your coat and outdoor shoes to brave the weather. The thick, dense fog, the biting cold, the hair-tugging wind.

'Before you can write about it, you must feel it, touch it, taste it, experience it,' the teacher says.

John Clare would agree with that. So what, you say. Who was John Clare?

Well, he was an unlikely poet too. He was born in the Northamptonshire village of Helpston in 1793. It was a typical village and his parents were typical villagers. Parker Clare, a farm labourer crippled with rheumatism by the age of forty, could read a little but neither of John's parents could write. The local schoolmaster encouraged John's unusual love of books but schooling ended at the age of twelve when he had to find a job. Not that he was a stranger to work. Or to braving the weather.

From early childhood he helped with seasonal tasks: crow scaring, weeding, stone picking, sheep tending, threshing, winnowing — an endless list of hard work all the year round under fierce summer sun or in frost and snow. This was only the start. He now had to earn money to help support his parents. He began by haymaking in the fields around his home. Or collecting dead sticks from the forest for firewood. Or doing odd jobs and running errands.

He wasn't a very good worker. He was rather lazy and preferred his books to hard physical graft which won him few friends amongst the villagers. Farm labourers weren't supposed to have ideas above their station. But John Clare was no ordinary ploughboy. He possessed both a remarkable memory and a fertile imagination. As a boy he wandered the woods, the heathland and the river banks around his

Helpston home observing the countryside in minute detail. He noticed the frosted cobweb hanging like delicate lace on the hawthorn hedge, the unusual texture of an insect's skin, the melancholy flapping of a heron's wings. Keen eyes made daily discoveries. It was like 'walking in a new world.'

One day when Clare was thirteen years old the village weaver showed him a tattered poetry book: *Seasons* by James Thomson. John wanted a copy of his own and pestered his father for the eighteen pence (one fifth of his weekly wage) to buy it from a bookshop in Stamford six miles away. When he arrived the bookshop was closed. He'd forgotten it was Sunday. Shops didn't open on Sundays. The following morning he walked again into the town having bribed someone to look after his ploughing horses. At half past six he was sitting on the steps outside the bookshop waiting for it to open.

The shopkeeper let him have the book for a shilling and Clare set off back to Helpston. But he couldn't wait. As he passed the grounds of Burghley House he climbed over the stone wall into the park. It wasn't done for a common labourer to be seen reading during working hours. Out of sight of the road he sat beneath a tree, opened his book and began to read. And read and read. He had forgotten the ploughing, forgotten everything. On that day he discovered poetry. The ideas stored away in his head since childhood found a voice. On the way back to Helpston he composed his first poem: *The Morning Walk*. Later he added other verses about his world of nature, including:

I felt that I'd a right to song
And sung – but in a timid strain
Of fondness for my native plain.

After the publication of his first collection, his poetry brought him success. He was invited to London by a rich patron. For a short time he was pampered as a pop star or famous footballer might be treated today. But gradually it all went sour. He never fitted into the world of high society. The tragedy was that his own people couldn't accept him either. Money troubles added to his problems. He now had a family of his own to support. Throughout his disappointments, however, Clare continued to write with great skill and affection about the countryside he knew and loved.

For everything I felt a love
The weeds below, the birds above.

Tormented and confused, suffering from mental illness, he died in a Northampton hospital on May 20th 1864.

Today he is recognised as a great poet and his memorial can be found along with that of Shakespeare, Wordsworth and Keats in Poet's Corner in Westminster Abbey. He is buried in Helpston churchyard next to his parents. An inscription reads:

'A poet is born not made.'

Perhaps so. But Clare believed that those childhood hours spent in the fields and woods around his home were the source of his wonderful words. Which is why your teacher will look out at the fog or the snow or the wind and say,

'Today we're going to do poetry.'

Tom Quincey

Becky's button

The five buttons were beautiful. They shone like glittering jewels against the dark blue cloth.

The five buttons were perfect. Arranged in a line like neatly parked cars, gleaming in a showroom window. Oh yes, the five buttons were wonderful.

Except for one thing.

There should have been six.

I could see the coat hanging on my peg from the cloakroom doorway. And down the front, button, button, button, button, gap, button.

My mum would kill me.

'You're not wearing your new coat for school,' she'd said at breakfast.

'Why not?'

'Because I said so.'

'What's the good of having a new coat if I can't wear it?'

'Don't be cheeky, my girl, or I'll take it back. Then you'll never get to wear it at all.'

She would as well. So I shut up about it and took another slice of toast.

'They don't make them like they used to,' mum said a few minutes later.

I wondered what she meant.

'Thrown together nowadays. Goodness knows what your gran will say when she sees it. She was a real seamstress she was. Every stitch done by hand.'

I realised she was talking about my coat. My brand new midnight blue coat with huge shiny buttons like sapphires. The style was brand new too. Only Georgina Tonsley at school had one the same.

'Look at it.'

She held it by the hood.

'Nothing to hang it up with, see. Within five minutes it'll be lying on the cloakroom floor. And these are loose already.'

She took hold of one of the buttons and tugged.

'They don't give you spares either.'

She hung the coat on the back of the chair and began to clear the table.

'Give me a hand Becky,' she said. 'I'm late enough as it is.'

Ten minutes later she was hurrying up the road to catch the shuttlebus into town, leaving me all alone. Alone with the coat.

She'd never know. I'd be home from school before she got in from work. The coat would be hanging on the back of the chair just as she'd left it.

What harm could it do?

Button, button, button, button, gap, button.

That's what harm it could do.

I must have lost it at lunch time.

A few pegs away from mine Georgina Tonsley's coat hung, complete with a full row of sapphires. My eyes flashed to the torn thread where my missing button had been, and then back to Georgina's.

Mum's words came back to me loud and clear.

'They don't give you any spares either.' Perhaps gran would sew it on for me. No-one was around. Afternoon school had ten minutes to go. I was

on an errand for Mrs Norman, my teacher. No-one would see.

It only took a second or two. My mum was right. The buttons were loose. One tug and it came away in my hand. Quickly I slipped it into *my* coat pocket and raced across to the mobile classroom with the message. When I got back to class Mr Driver, the headmaster, was coming out of the room. Inside there was silence. As I sat down I asked Laura what he had wanted.

Eagle-eyed Mrs Norman was looking our way.

'I'll tell you later,' Laura whispered. But not softly enough for bat-eared Mrs Norman.

'Not a sound everyone means you too, Becky and Laura. See me after school.'

So we were late leaving.

Ours were the only coats left in the cloakroom. I pulled mine on and followed Laura into the playground.

'What did Mr Driver want then?' I asked.

'He was moaning about the cloakroom,' she said.

'Everyone's coats were on the floor and he had to pick them up.'

My eyes widened.

'He said they were probably put back on the wrong pegs so make sure we got the right ones at the end of school.'

I looked at the row of buttons down the front of my coat. Button, button, button, button, gap, button. As I put my hand in my pocket I knew it would be empty.

But Georgina Tonsley would have a pleasant surprise when she searched hers.

Ian Addis

Memorial

Visit Grafton Underwood today and you'll find a typical English village. Stone cottages, thatched roofs, a slow, meandering brook, a duck-pond, tranquillity. Yet fifty years ago it was all so different.

The first clue can be found high on the west wall of the parish church where a stained glass window contains, unusually, the image of an aeroplane. A B17 Flying Fortress.

In a field about half a mile outside this village lies a second clue. A granite memorial. It marks the site of a huge wartime aerodrome that was home to the Eighth American Army Air Force.

It's hard to believe that acres of the surrounding countryside were swallowed up by concrete runways, control towers, living quarters for up to 3000 personnel and facilities which included a hospital, cinema and

chapel. Now the drone of heavy bombers preparing for take off has been replaced by the seasonal rumble of a tractor or combine harvester.

The stained-glass window and granite memorial however, remain like countless others around the world, a reminder of bravery and sacrifice in times of war.

Yet the true memorial to one such hero, probably the greatest of them all, cannot be found on the site of a wartime airfield. Leonard Cheshire was born in Chester in September 1917. His childhood ambition was to follow in his father's footsteps as Professor of Law at Oxford, although as a student he proved less than diligent. He preferred racing a supercharged Alfa Romeo sports car to poring over his books. When a dramatic crash put an end to this activity he took up flying, first in the University Air Squadron and then, at the outbreak of war in 1939, with the RAF.

He had hoped to fly single-seater fighter planes, like the glamorous Spitfire or Hurricane. Instead he found himself posted to a bomber squadron.

It was the beginning of an illustrious career. Group Captain Leonard Cheshire was decorated with three DSOs, a DFC and the most coveted award of all, the Victoria Cross. In all he flew exactly one hundred sorties over enemy territory. One hundred times he had gone out, bombed, endured gunfire, fought fear and tiredness and cold, exerted all his skill, exploited all his ingenuity and come back.

But one mission remained.

In August 1945 he was invited to join the crew of an American Air Force bomber as observer on a flight over Japan. The target, Nagasaki. The weapon, the atomic bomb. The effect upon the city was devastating. People directly subjected to the blast literally vanished beneath the terrible ball of fire, the searing heat leaving macabre shadows of their outline on the floor below. Buildings and vehicles exploded in flames. Crops and vegetation for miles around turned to blackened earth.

In one ten-millionth of a second 40, 000 men, women and children were left dead or dying.

As the mushroom cloud formed behind the aeroplane Leonard Cheshire suddenly sensed the horror the bomb had wrought. It was the greatest moment of truth in his life. The much decorated hero of war became a crusader for peace. From 1946 until his death in 1992 Cheshire devoted all his energies and meagre personal wealth to the care and welfare of the sick and impoverished. With his wife, Sue Ryder, herself already famous for working on behalf of the disabled, he expanded his ideas across the world. An international chain of small personalised settlements, Leonard Cheshire Homes, provided new options and opportunities for disabled people.

Today the Ryder-Cheshire Mission for the Relief of the Suffering has homes in every continent.

Happy is the man that findeth wisdom, and the man that getteth understanding: for the merchandise of it is better than the merchandise of silver, and the gain thereof than find gold.

That remains the true memorial to Leonard Cheshire, DSO, DFC, VC.

Charles Marlow

The Last Supper

Leonardo da Vinci was a genius. The colours he mixed and applied to canvas and plaster amazed the world. He was a gifted artist.

In 1493 the monks of Santa Maria delle Grazie asked Leonardo da Vinci to paint a mural in their monastery church. The subject of the painting was to be the Last Supper, showing Jesus sharing his last meal with his disciples. Leonardo decided to capture the very moment when Jesus was explaining to the disciples that one of them would betray him.

His research began. He planned to paint Jesus first; he needed someone who looked like his idea of Jesus. He found a young man who was ideal and agreed to be painted. Leonardo sketched, mixed and applied paint gazing at the kind, caring face with sensitive features. He placed Jesus in the centre of the mural behind a long table in front of three windows.

After weeks of painting, Leonardo paid the young man several gold coins. The picture of Jesus was finished. Now he had to search for others whose features reminded him of each one of the twelve disciples. The months passed as Leonardo searched and painted – James, John, Simon Peter and Andrew the four fishermen, James, Philip and Matthew (the one rich man amongst the disciples), Thomas, a carpenter, Simon, Bartholomew and Thaddeus. He experimented with new techniques, paints and varnishes as he sought to make his canvas come to life.

After four years the mural was finished except for the face of Judas Iscariot, the disciple who betrayed Jesus.

Leonardo studied the faces of criminals, murderers and vagrants but none looked like his idea of Judas. In desperation he toured the narrow streets of the city of Milan, late into the night, staring into doorways and peering into the unwashed faces of homeless thieves and drunkards. Would he ever find the man he was searching for? One evening, a ragged figure leapt out of the darkness and hurtled threateningly towards him.

The sight of the villain's face shocked Leonardo. Never had he seen such a menacing expression with eyes brimmed full of hatred. He had found his Judas Iscariot.

When the man had calmed down, Leonardo asked to paint him. The stranger agreed immediately.

The mural of the Last Supper could now be completed. Leonardo positioned the final disciple, prepared his paints and sketching sticks and paused to study the bone structure of the rough and haggard profile. He stared intently noticing that the lined, miserable face was drenched with tears.

The wretched fellow turned to face him. 'I was your idea of Jesus when you began this wonderful mural. Now, after four years of selfishness and greed, I am your idea of Judas Iscariot.'

Leonardo blended black into the startling white on his palette and began to outline the head of Judas with a threatening grey.

Sue Spooner

POEMS

A smile

A smile is such a lovely thing
It brightens up your face
And when it's gone it's hard to find
It's secret hiding place.

Yet, still more wonderful it is
To know what smiles can do
You smile at me. I smile at you.
And then one smile makes two.

Anonymous

From tomorrow

(A prayer from a child in a war-torn country)

From tomorrow on I shall be sad.
From tomorrow on.
Not today. Today I will be glad.
And every day no matter how bitter it may be,
I shall say:
From tomorrow on I shall be sad.
Not today.

Anonymous

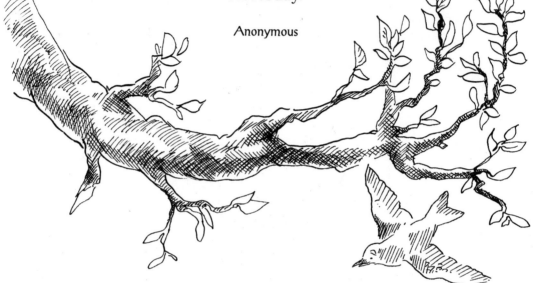

Blind girl

They say I am in darkness. I have heard
them speak of light that I shall never see.
They tell me of the brilliance of a bird.
Crimson and gold. The words sound sweet enough
upon the air, but what are words to me?

Standing beneath this pillar called a tree
this somehow friendly roughness I can touch,
I hear the birdsong falling wistfully
through the soft air toward my waiting ear.
Shall I miss gold or crimson overmuch?

For what is dark, when you have seen no light
And what is colour but an empty word?
Clasping this bark I stand in endless night
Hearing the wind move greenly through the leaves.
Hearing the gentle grieving of the bird.

Bill Scott

Truth

Sticks and stones may break my bones,
but words can also hurt me.
Stones and sticks break only skin,
while words are ghosts that haunt me.

Slant and curved the word-swords fall
to pierce and stick inside me.
Bats and bricks may ache through bones,
but words can mortify me.

Pain from words has left its scar
on mind and heart that's tender.
Cuts and bruises now have healed;
it's words that I remember.

Barrie Wade

Friendship

I fear it's very wrong of me,
And yet I must admit,
When someone offers friendship
I want the *whole* of it.
I don't want everybody else
To share my friends with me.
At least, I want one special one,
Who, indisputably,

Likes me much more than all the rest,
Who's always on my side,
Who never cares what others say,
Who lets me come and hide
Within his shadow, in his house
It doesn't matter where –
Who lets me simply be myself,
Who's always, always there.

Elizabeth Jennings

Time

Time means everything to me
Time past, time present, time future
Ordains my life.
I read and learn of kings and empires long ago.
The Roman road I walk along
Is an echo of long ago
Time, locked in museums of relics and dead scrolls.

Time is present to me now
What I do and say and think
I cannot hold and keep one single second
As I write this the moment has passed.

My hands stretch out to the future.
Is it bright with promise for me?
Please make my future a great adventure
For life is short to me.
The future will soon be the present
And one day I shall be old.

Pamela Scurr (age 11 years)

Books

I know a secret door into
a thousand scary places
where there's bloodsucking vampires
and things that don't have faces

A time machine that takes me
to fight with Francis Drake
and to fantastic jungles
on a magic silver snake

I can leap into the future
on the Starship Enterprise
or crawl into a rabbit hole
and quickly change my size

I'm solving a murder mystery
you can follow if you dare
while everyone round me
thinks I'm sitting on my chair.

I'm flying just like Superman
or riding painted wagons
I'm eating food in palaces
or killing fearsome dragons

I meet Alice and Verucca
Gandalf and Captain Hook
I have a quite amazing time
when I sit and read a book.

Mike Hoy

Daniel's rabbit

The rabbit wasn't old
but still he's dead.
He thinks he's a dog
Aunt Alison said,
the way he would sniff
and follow you or lie
stretched out on your bed.
But now when I whisper his name
he doesn't twitch at all
and Grandad's going to bury him
by the garden shed
and I never learned
how to pick him up
and now he's dead.

Fred Sedgwick

I told a lie today

I told a lie today
and it curled up inside me
like a steel hard spring.

It was quite a clever lie,
no one guessed the truth,
they believed me;

but I've carried the twist of it
at the centre of my body, all day,
and I think it's expanding,
filling me up,
making my eyes feel red.

Perhaps it's going to uncoil suddenly
and burst me open,
showing everyone what I'm really like.
I think I had better confess,
before I'm completely unwound.

Robin Mellor

Runaway

I've quarrelled with Laura
And upset Dad,
I've torn my jeans
And made Mum mad.
I'm in trouble at school
It's been a bad day,
And so I've decided
TO RUN AWAY.

I'll make sure they miss me
I'll shout and I'll scream,
Then bang a few doors
And make a scene.
I can just hear them
Down on their knees,
Mum, Dad and Laura
Begging
'COME BACK PLEASE.'

Out in the street
It's cold and it's dark,
Rain pours down
As I run through the park.
Soaked to the skin
I hurry along
Wondering where
My bad temper has gone.

Where am I going?
Where can I hide?
I need a new skin
To climb inside.
With different hair,
And different eyes,
A different shape,
The perfect disguise.

But if I got one
What use would it be?
Because I could never
Run away from ME.

Ian Addis

Go take a walk

I went for a walk.
I was angry, I was slighted.
I slammed the door behind me
And I shouted.
No-one listened.
Then the darkness fell around me,
And the drizzle drenched and cooled me,
And my footsteps seemed to calm me
As I stormed along the roadway.
Then my temper seemed to weaken
And my heartbeat seemed to quicken,
And my spirit seemed to lighten.
As I strode into the darkness
It took hold of my whole being.

Round the corner,
Through the Crescent,
Down the Road,
Across the Common,
In the darkness and the drizzle,
Away from the commotion
That had fuelled my explosion.

Orange light from lamps suspended
Was reflected by the puddles
And pierced the inner blindness
Of my anger and frustration.
Then my mind began to reason,
And my home began to beckon,
And I realised the anger
Was with me as much as others,
That the problem could be beaten
If I tried,
And if I wanted.

I got home from my walk
In the darkness and the drizzle.
Feeling wetter,
Feeling fresher,
Feeling better.

Ian Henderson-Begg

Remembrance Day

Poppies? Oh, miss,
can I take round the tray?
It's only history next.
We're into '45 –
I *know* who won the war,
no need to stay.

Old man wears his flower
with pride, his numbers dying now –
but that's no news.

Why buy? –
because I'm asked
because a flower looks good
to match my mate
not to seem too mean –
(what's tenpence anyway
to those of us who grew
with oranges, December lettuce and square fish?)
Yes, I'll wear it –
for a while.
Until it's lost
or maybe picked apart
during some boring television news
and then, some idle moment,
tossed.

Poppies? Who cares
as long as there's
some corner of a foreign field
to bring me pineapple, papaya
and my two weeks' patch of sun? –
But I'll still have one
if you really want.
It isn't quite my scene but then –
at least the colour's fun.

Old man stumbles
through November mud,
still keeps his silence
at the eleventh hour.

Judith Nicholls

The little house that smiled

In the beginning there was just a field
Of hedgerows, flowers and trees
With singing thrush and blackbird
And butterflies and bees.

Then, one day, the workmen came
And with them came the drone
Of lorries, diggers, bulldozers
Prepared to build a home.

They dug foundations
Built the walls
Then put a roof on top
And finally, when that was done,
The foreman said, 'Now stop.'

But the little house said anxiously
'What are you waiting for?
I'm still not finished
Can't you see?
I haven't got a door.'

So the workmen put a door in
All gaily painted red
But the little house was still so sad
And speaking firmly said:

'How can I feel happy?
How can I feel bright?
When I haven't any windows
To help let in the light.'

So the workmen put four windows in
Each gaily painted blue
But the little house looked sadly round
And told them what to do.

'You've got to tend the garden
Plant flowers, lawn and trees
To bring back all the wild life
The butterflies, birds and bees.

So the workmen made a garden
Just as the house had begged
But the little house was not finished yet

And it politely said:

'What I need is a family
With children large or small
To fill my kitchen, bedrooms, lounge
And bathroom, stairs and hall.'

Next day a furniture van arrived
Bringing cupboards, chairs and mats
A family with children three
A budgie, dog and cats.

Then the little house with one last plea
Looked up to the skies above
And uttered a prayer,
A simple prayer,
That its rooms be filled with love.

The family was happy
Loving, caring, kind,
And the little house that was once so sad
Became the house that smiled.

Ian Addis

Gran's photo

My Gran died
Before I was born.
Her picture
Is in a real, silver frame.
Mum says
I can't bring it to school.
It's the only one
We have.
Sometimes,
I look at Gran
And wish
I could sit
On her lap.

Anita Marie Sackett

A pirate song

'Where is the Treasure?'
Asked the pirate band.
'Hidden on an island,
Buried in the sand?'

'Where is the Treasure?'
Hear the pirates shout.
'Open up the treasure map
and let's find out.'

'Where is the Treasure?'
The pirates ask again.
The real Treasure's in your hearts
And there it will remain.

'You are my Treasure'
Says a pirate's mum,
'I've treasured you
Since you were begun.'

John Cotton

The golden cat

My golden cat had dappled sides;
No prince has worn so fine a cloak,
Patterned like sea-water where rides
The sun, or like the flower in oak
When the rough plank has been planed out,
Lovely as yellow mackerel skies
In moonlight, or a speckled trout.
Clear as swung honey were his eyes.

It was a wondrous daily thing
To look for, when his beautiful
Curved body gathered for a spring
That, light as any golden gull,
Flashed over the fine net of wire
Which my casement-window bars;
His leap was bright as tongues of fire,
And swift as autumn shooting-stars.

My cat was like a golden gift,
A golden myth of Grecian lore –
But things so bright, and things so swift,
Must vanish; and he is no more.

Eleanor Farjeon

Snowdrops

The weather was dreadful that morning
Bitter, with driving snow.
We were going to Gran's for the weekend,
But I didn't want to go.

I'd rather have gone to the pantomime
with Suzie, Katie and Pat.
Than sit cooped up in the back of the car,
With my Walkman's batteries flat.

The journey to Gran's was boring
My brother was a pain.
All the way there he ignored me,
Playing his computer game.

But the snowdrops were there to greet us
When, at long last, we arrived.
Smiling out of the window,
Welcoming us inside.

The weather this morning is dreadful
Bitter, with driving snow.
We're going to the pantomime today,
But I really don't want to go.

I'd rather be travelling to Gran's house
I wouldn't complain like before.
But Gran died last summer.
So we don't go anymore.

There are snowdrops in our window
And when I close my eyes
I can hear Gran's voice in the kitchen
And to me she's still alive.

Ian Addis

My grandpa

My grandpa is as round shouldered as a question mark
And is led about all day by his walking stick,
With teeth that aren't real,
Hidden behind a moustache that is,
While his memories simmer warmly
inside his crinkled paper bag of a face.
My grandpa,
Old and worn on the outside,
Sparky and fresh on the in.
For he often,
Shakes my hand with fifty pence pieces,
Makes sweets pop out from behind his ears,
Smokes all day like a train
then laughs like one as well.
Plays jokes on my mother
as he tries to freshen her face with a smile,
And then tells me stories that electrify my brain.
But best of all,
When my dad loses his temper,
Grandpa just tells him
TO SIT DOWN AND BEHAVE HIMSELF.
Good old grandpa.

Ian Souter

Parent free zone

Parents please note that from now on,
our room is
a 'Parent Free Zone'.

There will be no spying
under the pretence
of tidying up.

There will be no banning
of television programmes
because our room
is a tip,

no complaints about noise,
or remarks about the ceiling
caving in.

No disturbing the dirty clothes
that have festered in piles
for weeks.

No removal of coffee cups
where green mould
has taken a hold.
(These have been left there
for scientific research purposes.)

No reading of letters
to gain unauthorised information
which may be used against us
at a later date.
No searching through school bags
to discover if we've done our homework
or unearth forgotten notes.

Our room is a 'Parent Free Zone'
and a notice is pinned to the door.
But just a minute,
there's something wrong...
MUM – WHY HAVEN'T YOU MADE OUR BEDS?

Brian Moses

Brothers and sisters

When we fall out
(which we often do)
My nan says: 'You
can pick your friends but
you can't pick your relatives.'
So that is why I'm stuck with Gus
And Mum is stuck with both of us.

If I say 'black'
Then he'll say 'white'
He's always trying to start a fight.
He moans a lot and says he wishes
I'd sometimes let *him* wash the dishes.
How come he *always* has to dry?
But I'm the oldest, *that* is why.

And yet, you know, the fun we've had
I'd have to say he's not so bad –
He makes me laugh and he's on my side
When the chips are down and I'd like to hide.
So secretly, I like my brother
And if I could pick, I'd pick no other.

Jane Wright

Those were the days

Mum always says she scrimped and saved,
we have it too easy today,
there's nothing we have to work for
and everything comes our way.

'When I was a girl,' she says,
'My clothes were hand-me-down,
I had older brothers and sisters,
there wasn't much money around.'

'We made our own entertainment,
dressed up or played in the street,
our treats were Saturday pictures
with sixpence to spend on sweets.'

'If ever a teacher walloped us,
we wouldn't have dared tell Mum,
wait till your Dad gets home, she'd say,
then he'd have clouted us one.'

Oh those were the days, when you were young Mum,
long ago before my birth,
when televisions were black and white
and dinosaurs ruled the Earth!

Brian Moses

Mum

My mum
cleans me
feeds me
helps me
and mends me

She also
clothes me
tidies me
sweet dreams me
and tends me.

She tries to
homework me
library me
organise me
and please me.

Sometimes she has been known to
scold me
warn me
anger me
and tease me.

However, she's great when she
birthday presents me
pocket moneys me
Easter Eggs me
and just surprises me.

But best of all is when mum
cuddles me
tickles me
praises me
and simply IDOLISES ME!

Ian Souter

New pet

We've something new at our house now,
A something soft and small.
But though it cries and wiggles so,
It's not a pig at all!

It drinks just milk and gulps it down
Till it looks very fat.
It can't chase mice; do you know why?
It isn't any cat!

It cries at night; I guess that's 'cause
It's lonely for its mother.
No, it's not a puppy dog.
It's a baby brother!

Lois F. Pasley

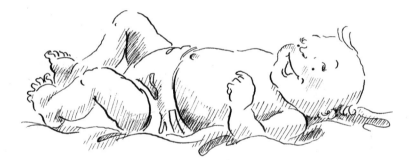

Birth

Head first, purple like a prune,
unplugged from spongy silence
I cringe at the sting of brightness.

The journey's over.

Slapped into anger I learn language,
thump fists, kick.

The journey begins.

Gina Douthwaite

Millions of people

There are millions of people
In millions of places
And all of the people
Have different faces.
The tilt of the nose
May vary a bit;
The slant of the eye,
The curve of the lip.
You may look and look
At the fats and the thins
But no two are alike –
'Cept identical twins.
And they too may differ,
Even as we,
In some little way
That you cannot see.
No one can explain it
No one is to blame –
There are millions of people
And no two the same.

Jane W. Krows

No difference

Small as a peanut
Big as a giant
But we're all the same size
When we turn off the light.

Rich as a sultan
Poor as a mite
We're all worth the same
When we turn off the light.

Red, black or orange
Yellow or white
We all look the same
When we turn off the light.

So maybe the way
To make things alright
Is for God to reach out
And turn off the light.

Shel Silverstein

One child

One child weak
One child strong
One child right
One child wrong.

One child loved
One child not
One child remembered
The other forgot.

One child laughs
One child cries
One child lives
The other dies.

Rachael Gray (age 12 years)

Song of the refugee child

I may be little but let me sing,
I may be a child but let me in;
what does it matter if I read or write?
you'll send me to war to learn to fight.
I am the refugee child.

I am the hungry of a hundred lands,
mine is the blood that stains the white sands,
but I'll climb your barbed wire and walls of stone
and find a free place to make a new home.
I am the refugee child.

I am the dispossessed, wandering one,
you can't kill me with your bomb and your gun;
I am the face that looks out from the night
towards your rich window with its warmth and its light.
I am the refugee child.

I am a child of the family called Poor
and I am coming to knock on your door;
I may be little but let me sing,
I may be a child but you must let me in.
I am the refugee child.

Robin Mellor

Our street

We played with dustbin lids
and sticks
With pistols,
We attacked the Indians
Of the next road,
Or swung with skipping ropes
From the green lamppost bars.
'You'll hang yourselves,' said a passer-by.
We used the post for rounders.
Ball bouncing on the front doors.
'Go play up yer own end of the street,'
Old Ma King would shout.
'I can see yer, I'll tell your mum!'
People chatted to each other
On their way to work.
Sirens hooted at dinner time.
And at 5.30, apronned factory
workers treaded home to tea.
We were not allowed to
street play on Sundays.
'You can play in the back yard
If you don't make a noise!'

Coronation year
We had a party, races
And competitions,
Held in the factory
During the rain.
'We won the cup for the best
decorated street.'
We chanted to our rivals.
Flags, bunting and
fancy windows.
Ours had a golden miniature
coach, on a blue velvet cloth.
The street was friendly then,
And we knew everyone in the road.
But no longer is it neighbourly and safe.
Cars line the street
And people rarely walk along the pavements.
The shop has changed hands yet once again.
And only sell two kinds of biscuits!
'They won't last long!'
The street is dead.
Old Ma King died years ago
And my mum died this year.

Anita Marie Sackett

The new house

I don't much like this bedroom
The bedroom doesn't care for me
It looks at me like a policeman
Inspecting a refugee.

The bathroom doesn't feel like home at all
Feels more like an empty space
And the mirror seems used to staring at
A completely different face.

I don't like the smell of the kitchen
Don't like the garden or the rain
Feels like a deserted station
Where I'm waiting for a train.

I can't kick a ball against this wall
I can't build a house in this tree
And the streets are as quiet and deserted
As the local cemetery.

I don't like the look of the kids next door
Playing in the beat up car
Why do they stand and stare at me?
Who do they think they are?

The big boy's coming over
He's just about my height
Why has he got a brick in his hand?
Is he going to pick a fight?

But he asks us into their garden
He tells us his name is Ben
And Jane is the name of his sister
And will we help them build their den.

We can't get it finished by dinner time
We won't get it finished by tea
But there'll be plenty of time in the days ahead
For Ben, Jane, Andy and me.

Gareth Owen

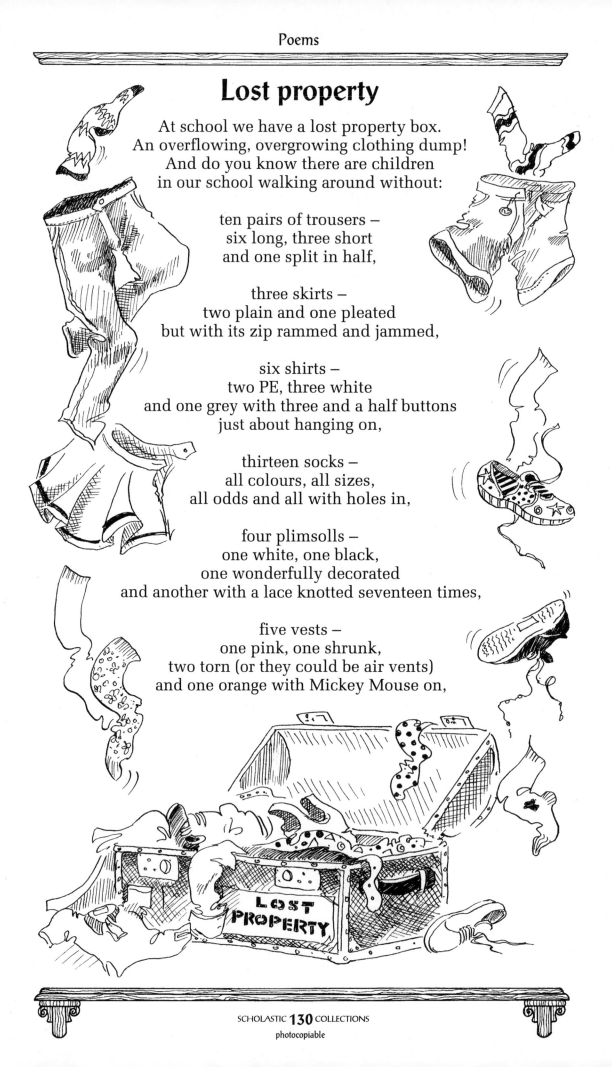

Lost property

At school we have a lost property box.
An overflowing, overgrowing clothing dump!
And do you know there are children
in our school walking around without:

ten pairs of trousers –
six long, three short
and one split in half,

three skirts –
two plain and one pleated
but with its zip rammed and jammed,

six shirts –
two PE, three white
and one grey with three and a half buttons
just about hanging on,

thirteen socks –
all colours, all sizes,
all odds and all with holes in,

four plimsolls –
one white, one black,
one wonderfully decorated
and another with a lace knotted seventeen times,

five vests –
one pink, one shrunk,
two torn (or they could be air vents)
and one orange with Mickey Mouse on,

seven hats –
five bobble, one balaclava
and one that looks like my aunty's tea cosy,

two pairs of underpants,
one with Superman flying across
and the other with only the elastic remaining,

and finally one slightly chipped white tooth
which I think is probably plastic
and has dropped off a set of joke teeth.

Now we've asked and we've searched
but we can't find these undressed creatures.
I'm now really beginning to believe
that it could all belong to the teachers!

Ian Souter

The new lad

There's a new lad in our class,
all the way from China.
His Dad's at the army base,
his Mum runs the Hongyiang Diner.

He seems a little different to us,
his skin is a yellowy-brown.
He doesn't understand much,
his face wears a constant frown.

He draws red fiery dragons
when he's meant to be reading his book.
Our teacher keeps on giving him
her sympathetic look.

Then out today at playtime
he joined in our game with a ball.
He scored two brilliant goals,
now we don't think he's different at all.

Brian Moses

A right to song

The old man sat at the water's edge
And watched the stream pass by,
Not with a careless, hasty glance,
But a countryman's knowing eye.
For the current carried memories
That cleared his fuddled brain,
And images of childhood
Filled his mind again.

There were the fields for haymaking,
There were the crows to scare,
There were the chestnut trees to climb
And there were the nuts to share.
There were the books to hide away,
To read in a secret place,
Away from the teasing village boys
Who thought they brought disgrace.
There were the words that poured from his pen,
Claiming his right to song,
Finding a voice in poetry –
Words that live on and on.

The old man sat at the water's edge
And sadly watched the stream
As it dashed away his memories
As it swallowed up his dream.
While on the bridge, the onlookers
Gathered together to stare
To nudge and point and whisper,
'He used to be John Clare.'

Ian Addis

The watchers on the shore

Still was the air as they left that night
The men who brave the deep
With ropes and nets they manned their boats
While you and I were asleep
And with sails hoisted high
They watched the sky
As storm clouds awakened their dread
But you and I tossed in sheets so warm
For you and I were abed.

Wild was the wind as they stood that night
The womenfolk on the strand
With cloaks and shawls they braved the spray
While you and I slept sound
And with tearful gaze
they stared at the waves
Till their eyes could see no more
No mermaid song, no lullabies
For the watchers on the shore.

Ian Addis

Seal-song

In a faintly blue-tinged crystal sea
a seal has turned to look at me,
deep black eyes and body long,
it sings its own seal-song.

'Oh keep my waters deep and fresh
and let there be many fish,
let all my friends swim next to me
this is a seal's true wish.

And keep the blackness from the waves
and poison from the air,
let gulls and cormorants dive within
our waters, while we're there.

Let our friends, who live on land,
know the sea is deep and long,
and there is room for everyone
who can hear my own seal-song.'

In a faintly blue-tinged crystal sea
a seal has turned to look at me,
deep black eyes and body long,
it sings its own seal-song.

Robin Mellor

Names

My name is 'Couldn't care less',
just let the forests die.
My name is 'Can't be bothered',
who cares about holes in the sky?

My name is 'I'm too busy',
let someone else do the worrying,
there's nothing that I can do
if the ice caps are wearing thin.

My name is 'Leave me alone',
just don't go preaching to me.
Gossip is what I care about
not oil that's spilt in the sea.

My name is 'I'm alright Jack',
there's really no cause for alarm.
Hens are silly birds, who cares
if they suffer at the factory farm?

Who cares about global warming,
I like a spot of hot weather.
My name is 'Sit on the fence',
my name is 'All of a dither'.

So stop saying what I should think,
I don't want to believe what I'm told.
My name is 'Hope it will go away',
My name is 'Don't get involved'.

And who do you think you are,
telling us all we should worry?
WELL, MY NAME'S A WARNING FROM FUTURE YEARS,
IT'S 'LISTEN OR YOU'LL BE SORRY'.

Brian Moses

My heart beats

My spirits tighten
when the television protests:

seas under threat,
oil pollution,
nuclear power.
When the radio complains of:

mountains of rubbish,
wastage of energy,
global warming.

When the newspaper headlines cry:

acid rain,
hole in the ozone layer,
destroying the rain forests.

My spirits tighten.

But my heart beats
when I think of:

nothing moving,
only sunshine colouring in
as it spills itself across
a freshly made morning.

When I imagine:

snowflakes furtively
dusting themselves
in their talcum powder cleanliness
across an unsuspecting countryside.

When I listen:

to the night's silence
wrapping itself gently around me,
to await the creation
of a new born day.
My heart beats.

Ian Souter

Footpath from summer

High and dry up on the beach
where sleepy summer tides don't reach
a tangled fringe of orange nets,
washed-white wood, slung cigarettes
rest with caved-in Cola cans,
black seaweed stretches out clawed hands
as though to beckon to the sea,
to plead – *from rubbish wash me free.*

Gina Douthwaite

At the end of a school day

It is the end of a school day
and down the long drive
come bag-swinging, shouting children.
Deafened, the sky winces.
the sun gapes in surprise.

Suddenly the runners skid to a stop,
stand still and stare
at a small hedgehog
curled-up on the tarmac
like an old, frayed cricket ball.

A girl dumps her bag, tiptoes forward
and gingerly, so gingerly
carries the creature
to the safety of a shady hedge.
Then steps back, watching.

Girl, children, sky and sun
hold their breath.
There is a silence,
a moment to remember
on this warm afternoon in June.

Wes Magee

Trees

Trees are always homes
to every sort of creature,
in an empty landscape
a tree is a special feature.

Trees can be deciduous,
pine trees are coniferous,
trees will never hurt you,
no tree is carnivorous!

So snuggle up to a sycamore,
cuddle close to a pine,
wrap your arms around an oak,
enjoy a joke with a lime.

A tree will always listen,
tell you troubles to a tree.
To the mystery of life
an ash may hold the key.

So treat a tree politely,
show it you're sincere.
Long after we have disappeared,
trees will still be here.

Brian Moses

Death of the elms

The trees were once tall,
And fun to climb on.
They shaded us from the sun,
And we played around them.

But now they are gone,
And all that is left,
Are tree stumps and logs
And scattered sawdust.

Gone is the noise of the chain saws,
The clashing of trees on the ground
And the crackles of the fire
That burnt up the trees' old branches,
The elm trees are dead.

Catherine Englishby (age 11 years)

Museum piece

Imagine not knowing about buttercups,
never seeing them light up the grass.
Imagine if one day you found one by chance,
how you'd keep it safe underneath glass.

Imagine missing the deep sea of yellow
if buttercups were incredibly rare.
You couldn't possibly hold one under
your chin to see a butter mark there!

You couldn't watch cows go paddling
in buttercups up to their knees.
You'd lock every flower up in a case
or preserve it in the deep-freeze.

Next time you find yellow buttercups
shining jewel-like under the sun,
look at a flower as though it were gold,
imagine it's the last precious one.

Imagine if nobody cares for the earth,
if buttercups die in front of your eyes –
that tiny frail flower you hold in your hand
might well be the world's greatest prize!

Moira Andrew

Celebration

If cherries were rubies
we'd treasure them.
If raindrops were diamonds
we'd cherish them.
If bluebells were sapphires
we'd honour them.
If oak trees were icons
we'd worship them.

If water was wine
we'd savour it.
If sunshine were bullion
we'd salt it away.
If Earth were a festival
we'd celebrate.
Let's drink to our riches,
make music and dance!

Moira Andrew

Hindu poem

Sky so bright
Blue and light
Stars – how many have you?
Countless stars
Countless times
Shall our God be praised now.
Forest green
Cool, serene,
Leaves – how many have you?
Countless leaves
Countless times
Shall our God be praised now.

Anonymous

Courage of life

Without belittling the courage
with which men have died,
We should not forget those acts of courage
with which men... have lived.
The courage of life
is often a less dramatic spectacle
than the courage of a final moment;
but it is not less a magnificent mixture
of triumph and tragedy.

John F. Kennedy

Easter

The year turns at Easter time.

Button buds collect on the branches
and like a sprinkling of young yellow suns,
bright daffodils colour
the hibernating fields and hedgerows.

The year turns, slowly and silently, into spring
and everywhere the new born chicks, lambs and fledglings
struggle to be seen, heard and noticed.
Out of the grey, bare days of the weak winter
the sacred strength of spring emerges.

The year turns and Mother Earth lifts her ashen face
to the pale blue of the brightening sky.
In celebration she pushes up
the timeclocks of the ages –
a flourish of flowers, a blast of blossom.

John Rice

Annunciation – Leonardo da Vinci

Here is the news today, my friend:
a baby's on His way
climbing through the mystery
into the day.

Climbing through the mystery
where the girl is waiting
startled, honoured, frightened-eyed,
just anticipating.

Startled, honoured, frightened-eyed –
we wait at Christmas time
for the giving visitor,
his presents and his rhyme.

For the giving visitor
with his gift of gold
to the young girl waiting
in the winter cold.
To the young girl waiting
things are what they seem:
a winged person in the grass
like a summer-garden dream.

A winged person in the grass
in the cloak of red and green...
and the girl thinks of an unborn child
only God has seen.

Fred Sedgwick

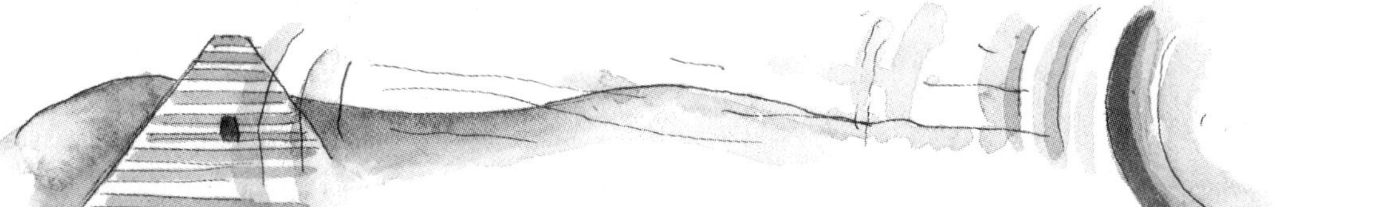

The Pharaoh addresses his god, the sun

You created the earth
when you were far away –
men, cattle, all flocks –
everything on earth
moving with legs,
creeping, stalking, or striding,
or flying and gliding above with wings.
Foreign countries
and the land of Egypt:
you placed every man in his place
and you provide his food.

You are the Creator of Months
and the Maker of Days.
You are the Counter of Hours!

You shine on the eastern horizon
and fill the whole earth with your beauty
and while you are far away
your beams shine in every face.

When you shine
creatures live.
When you set
they die.
You yourself
are lifetime.
In you do creatures live.

Living disc,
Lord of all that was created
and which exists!
your beams have brightened
the whole earth.

Fred Sedgwick

New Year

This night
of all the nights
is the year's last.
All, all
the other nights
are gone, are past...

After
the evening, with
its fading light,
put the lid
on the hour
and close it tight.

Close up
your tired eye;
close up the day.
Bid the old year
Goodbye,
and come away.

Jean Kenward

SONGS
Greetings

Gillian Parker

1. Sa - laam, Sha - lom, Na -
2. We might shake hands in
3. If you don't know the

mas - te, Bon - jour, Sa - lut, Good day. We
friend - ship, Red In - di - ans say, 'HOW'. We
right words To say a warm 'Hel - lo', Just

greet each oth - er round the world In ma - ny differ - ent ways.
raise our hats or kiss both cheeks Or click our heels and bow.
nod your head and give a smile, Then ev - ery - one will know!

Save the children

David Coysh

2. Arms outstretched to one another,
Helping hands to guide the way.
Simply sharing means we're caring –
Just listen, hear what they say.

Chorus

3. Bless our children, don't forget them;
They need friends who understand
That each life deserves some meaning –
We'll stretch our helping hands.

Your ray of light

Clive Barnwell

1. As you jour-ney on, and the road is long, Which way should you turn?

Leav-ing what you knew for a world that's new,

Such a lot to learn. Ev-ery-thing a-round con -

fus - es you. Ev-ery-thing a-round is strange.

When the dark - ness comes in sight, I will be your

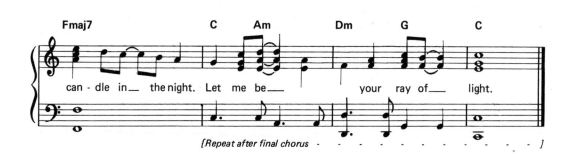

can - dle in_ the night. Let me be_ your ray of_ light.

[Repeat after final chorus - - - - - - - - - -]

2. As you journey on, learning right from wrong,
You'll find where to turn.
Soon you find that you know just what to do,
And what you must learn.
Everything around amuses you.
People turn around and say:

Chorus

3. As you journey on, now the road's not long,
You know where to turn.
There are others who find that, just like you,
They've a lot to learn.
Everything around confuses them.
You can turn around and say:

Chorus

I want to say thank you

Clive Barnwell

Why does an elephant grow so big?

Clive Barnwell

My friend

Clive Barnwell

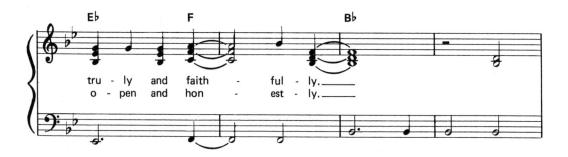

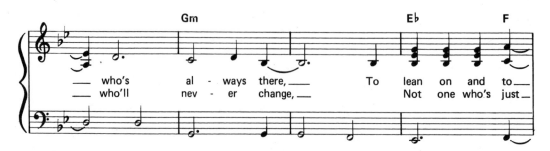

de - pend. And when things are bad
pre - tend. And when things are bad

I'll be pleased I had you my friend
I'll be pleased I had you my friend

Chorus

1. You can climb the high - est moun-tain, You can swim the deep-est
2. You can tread the dark - est path-way, You can climb the tall - est

seas, If you've a friend to help with all of
trees, If you've a friend to help with all of

these. You can solve the great - est prob - lems, See the race out to the
these. You can make the right de - cis - ions, There'll be no-thing you can't

[2nd time repeat Chorus 1]

end, If you've got a friend. (You can)
mend, If you've got a friend.

A handful of rice

David Moses

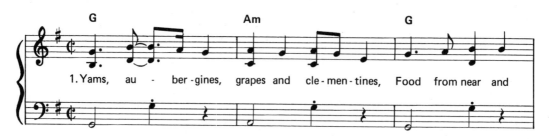

1. Yams, au - ber - gines, grapes and cle - men - tines, Food from near and

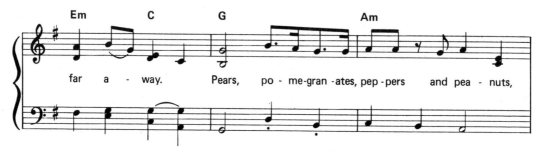

far a - way. Pears, po - me-gran -ates, pep - pers and pea - nuts,

What shall we buy to eat to - day? *Chorus* How would it be if we

just ate rice, No-thing but a hand - ful of plain boiled rice, Like the

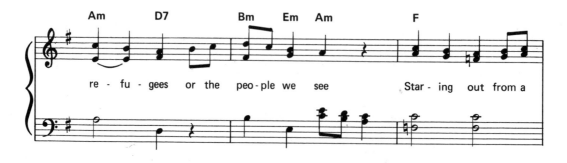

re - fu - gees or the peo - ple we see Star - ing out from a

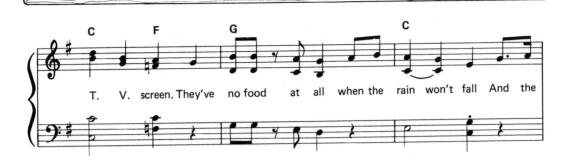

T. V. screen. They've no food at all when the rain won't fall And the crops don't grow. So we all need to help a-ny way we can When the crops won't grow.

2. Trout, tuna fish, hake and halibut,
Food from near and far away.
Clams, calamari, cockles and cod fish
What shall we buy to eat today?

Chorus
How would it be if we just ate maize,
Trying to make it last us for days and days,
Like the refugees... etc.

3. Ribs, shish kebab, chow mien, fish and chips,
Food from near and far away
Beans, biriani, bangers and burgers,
What shall we buy to eat today?

Chorus
How would it be if we just didn't eat
Lying on the ground in the dust and heat,
Like the refugees... etc.

How it feels to be hungry

David Moses

1. Do you know the way it feels to be hun-gry and you need a bis-cuit or a sweet? When you think a-bout the smell of your fa-vour-ite food, do you long for some-thing to eat? *Chorus* We are the hun-gry child-ren. Feed us. We are the hun-gry child-ren. Feed us. Do you. . .

2. Do you know the way it feels to be hungry when lunch is ages away
Eating your breakfast seems so long ago and you've only just come in from play?

Chorus

3. Do you know the way it feels to be hungry when there's no money left to buy food
Or you've been sent to bed with nothing to eat because you were naughty or rude?

Chorus

4. Do you know the way it feels to be hungry and your inside's empty as the air?
Just a handful of rice has to last you all day, nothing else, there's no more to spare.

Chorus

5. Do you know the way it feels to be hungry when the truck with the rice doesn't come?
There'll be no food today, and nothing to do but to lie there crying in the sun.

Chorus

Help us to choose what to do and say

Traditional Peruvian folk tune, words by David Moses

1. Spi-rit of the pa-tient and the kind, show us all the good there is to find. Spi-rit of the love that helps us live, Show us we can all learn to for-give. Spi-rit of love, light our way, help us to choose what to do and say.

2. Spirit of the peaceful and the strong,
show us what is right and what is wrong.
Spirit of the joy we all can know,
show us how to live and how to grow.
Spirit of love, light our way.
Help us to choose what to do and say.

I can be quiet

David Moses

1. I can be qui - et, thought - ful and qui - et in - side.

In my head I feel me, look - ing out.

I can be qui - et, thought - ful and qui - et in - side.

In my head, some - one whis - pers my name soft - ly.

2. I can be quiet, thoughtful and quiet inside.
In my heart there is love, reaching out.
I can be quiet, thoughtful and quiet inside.
Is that voice in my head and my heart you Lord?

I've got a friend called Albert

David Moses

2. I've got a friend called Mary, Mary is her name.
When she comes to my house, we like to play.
We go 'Clap clap clap, clap clap clap, clap clap clap again;
Clap clap clap' with Mary, 'cause Mary is her name.

(clap hands)

3. I've got a friend called Leroy, Leroy is his name.
When he comes to my house, we like to play.
We put one hand up, one hand down, up and down again;
Up and down with Leroy, 'cause Leroy is his name.

(raise and lower hand)

4. I've got a friend called Asha, Asha is her name.
When she comes to my house, we like to play.
We go 'Yes yes yes, no no no, yes yes yes again;
Yes and no with Asha, 'cause Asha is her name.

(nod and shake head)

Loulou the lollipop lady

David Moses

1. Loulou the lollipop lady stands at the side of the road. Look to the left, Look to the right, Crossing with Loulou is quite all-right. Loulou the lollipop lady makes all the motor cars stop. When she puts her sign up, the children all line up, Then sensibly walk across.

2. Loulou the lollipop lady stands with her sign in the air.
Patiently wait by the edge of the road,
Loulou will say when it's safe to go.
Loulou the lollipop lady out in the fog, rain and frost;

Praise the Lord

Ian Henderson-Begg

1. Can you feel the spring in the air? As the world a-wakes life is there. As new shoots bright and green Break the sur-face and are seen, Praise the Lord for all that we share.

Chorus
Praise the Lord, He is there, In the new life we see all a-round. Praise the Lord, He is here. Let our songs fill His world with their sound.

2. Can you feel the warmth of the sun?
As the days draw out, winter's done.
All of life, so it seems,
Turns its face to feel the beams.
Praise the Lord for springtime has come.

Chorus

3. Can you feel the care and the love
That he gives the world from above?
Every bird, every tree,
Every insect that we see,
He has made, for the world is His dove.

Chorus

4. Can you feel your mind start to know
From all you see that it's so?
That a God strong and true
Has created me and you,
And He helps us flourish and grow.

The litter song

Andrew Jackson

Chorus

Lit-ter, lit-ter, lit-ter ev-ry-where. Lit-ter, lit-ter, do we real-ly care? The world is full of rub-bish.___ It real-ly is a mess. We ought to clean it up so it will look its best. 1. There's it will look its best. 2. So

Verse

lit-ter on the pave-ment and there's lit-ter on the street. There's lit-ter al-most ev-'ry-where You want to put your feet. There's

lit - ter in the park, Oh, what are we to do? If

some - one's going to clear it up, It's up to me and you. There's

2. There's litter on the pavement,
And there's litter on the street.
There's litter almost everywhere
You want to put your feet.
There's litter in the park
Oh what are we to do?
If someone's going to clear it up,
It's up to me and you.

Chorus

So if you have a wrapper,
Or an empty cola tin,
Just put it in your pocket
till you find yourself a bin.
Try to keep things tidy,
Don't put things on the floor,
We don't want to see your litter,
We don't want it any more.

You do it all for me

Ian Henderson-Begg

1. When you see some-one old With a bag or a load, Do you stop and lend them a hand?_____ If you do it for one Of my daugh-ters or my sons, Then you do it all for me._____

2. When you see someone fall,
Or you hear someone call,
Do you stop to see what is wrong?

Chorus

3. When a stranger or friend
Needs help to the end,
Do you offer help on the way?

Chorus

4. At the end of each day
Can you honestly say
That you answered when someone called?

Chorus

A promise

Music by Ralph E. Pearce, words by Sue Spooner

Bossa Nova

1. Our world will keep on turn - ing, The seas, the land, the air.
Each day asks us to prom - ise, "Will you use my gifts and share?"

Chorus
Lord I will keep my prom - ise In all I say and do. This day and all that fol - low, I'll care

1. for the world and you. 2. The for the world and you.

2. The world is filled with plenty,
Yet we don't seem to share.
The millions go hungry,
Can we refuse to care?

Chorus

Kaleidoscope

Ann Bryant

Chorus G

You can hold a kal - ei - do - scope___ of col - ours,

D

See the pat - terns that you hold. There are shapes you've ne - ver ev - er

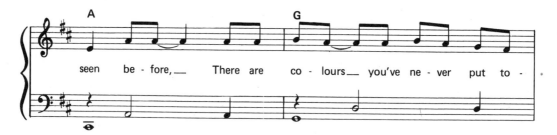

A   G

seen be - fore,___ There are co - lours___ you've ne - ver put to -

A   D   Bm

ge - ther be - fore___ Be - cause the world___ is made up of

A7   D   *Fine* G

pat - terns ga - lore.   1. My   home is

way up high;— my home is white and round; My home is

float - ing on wa - ter; and my home is un - der-ground. My home is

in the for - est;— my home is mud - dy brown; My home is

on the hill - side; and my home is in the town. You can

Chorus

2. I wash my hair on Sundays; I grind the flour for bread;
I help my dad spear fishes; I can't get out of bed;
I've never left my village; I've seen the world by plane;
I wish we'd get some sunshine; and I sit and pray for rain.

Chorus

Don't throw grandad away

Peter Morrell

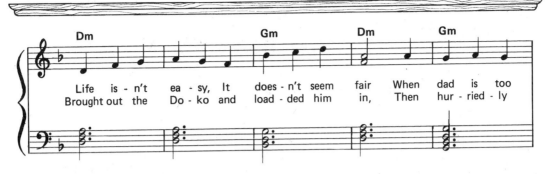

Life is - n't ea - sy, It does - n't seem fair When dad is too
Brought out the Do - ko and load - ded him in, Then hur - ried - ly

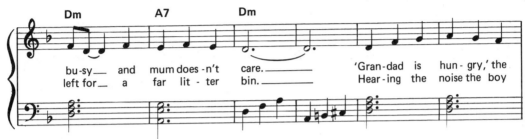

bu - sy__ and mum does - n't care.____ 'Gran - dad is hun - gry,' the
left for__ a far lit - ter bin.____ Hear - ing the noise the boy

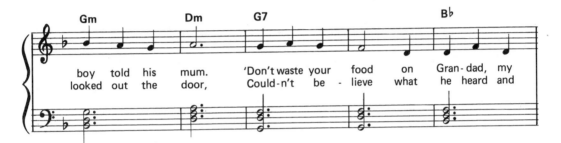

boy told his mum. 'Don't waste your food on Gran - dad, my
looked out the door, Could - n't be - lieve what he heard and

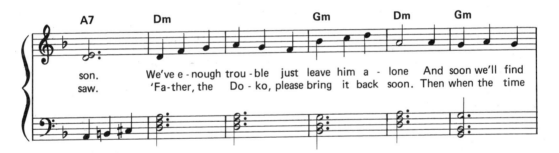

son. We've e - nough trou - ble just leave him a - lone And soon we'll find
saw. 'Fa - ther, the Do - ko, please bring it back soon. Then when the time

Gran - dad a home of his own.' 'But
comes, I'll throw you a - way too.' 'So

Seal song

Music by Peter Morrell, words by Robin Mellor

In a faint-ly blue tinged

crys-tal sea _____ a seal has turned to look at me, *mf*

deep black eyes and bo-dy long, it sings it's own seal-

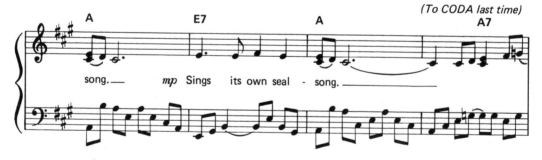

song. ___ *mp* Sings its own seal - song. _____

1. 'Oh keep my wa-ters deep and fresh _____ and let there be so ma-ny
2. And keep the black-ness from the waves _____ and keep the poi-son from the
3. And let our friends who live on land _____ know that the sea is deep and

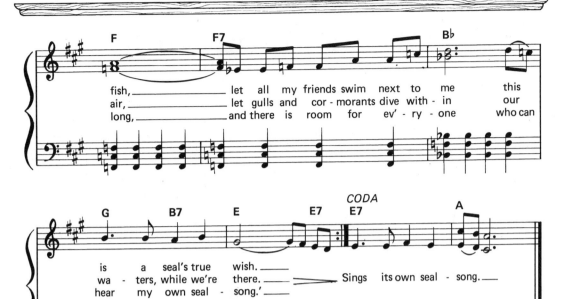

fish, _____ let all my friends swim next to me this
air, _____ let gulls and cor - morants dive with - in our
long, _____ and there is room for ev' - ry - one who can

is a seal's true wish. ____
wa - ters, while we're there. ____ Sings its own seal - song. ____
hear my own seal - song.' ____

Chorus:
In a faintly blue-tinged crystal sea
a seal has turned to look at me,
deep black eyes and body long,
it sings its own seal-song.

1. 'Oh keep my waters deep and fresh
and let there be so many fish,
let all my friends swim next to me
this is a seal's true wish.

2. And keep the blackness from the waves
And keep the poison from the air,
let gulls and cormorants dive within
our waters, while we're there.

3. And let our friends who live on land,
know that the sea is deep and long,
and there is room for everyone
who can hear my own seal-song.'

4. In a faintly blue-tinged crystal sea
a seal has turned to look at me,
deep black eyes and body long,
it sings its own seal-song.

Colours of the world

Peter Morrell

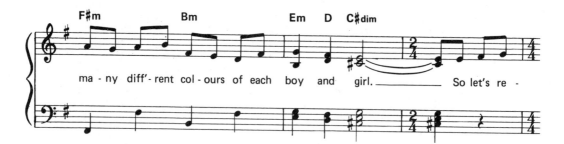

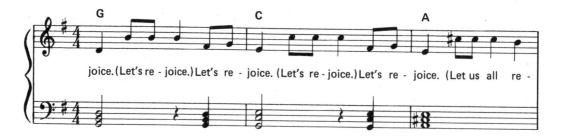

G　　　　　**Bm**　　　　　**Am**

Ⓡ is for Res - pect we have for ev' - ry - thing on Earth,
Ⓑeau - ty all a - round us black and yel - low, pink and white,

F　　　　　**Am**　　　　　**C**　　　**C#dim**

Ⓐwe and won - der at the pow'r of Na - ture from its birth.
Ⓞn - ly we can change our thoughts on what is wrong and right.

Dm　　　　　**G**　　　　　**C**　　　　　**Am**

Ⓘn - di - vid - ual be - ings born to love and care and be
Ⓦe can do it, me and you it when we rise a - bove, and

1. **F**　　　　　**Am**　　　　　**D7**

Ⓝeigh - bours to all creeds and ra - ces ev' - ry - one we see.

CODA

2. **F**　　　　　**C**　　　**C dim 7**　**D7**　　**C**　**D7**　**G**

paint our World with col - ours from our Rain - bow of Love. The

The highlighted letters (Ⓡ) spell out RAINBOW!

A prayer

Music by Ralph E. Pearce, words by Sue Spooner

Slowly

mp Oh— Je - sus al - ways stay with me. Oh— Je - sus please watch ov - er

me. Oh— Je - sus show me how to care——— Oh Je - sus

I know you'll be there. Oh— Je - sus al - ways stay with me Oh

Je - sus please watch ov - er me. A - men. (A - men) A -

men. (A - men.) A - men. (A - - men.)

Oh Jesus always stay with me,
Oh Jesus please watch over me,
Oh Jesus show me how to care,
Oh Jesus I know you'll be there.
Oh Jesus always stay with me,
Oh Jesus please watch over me,
Amen. Amen. Amen. Amen. Amen. Amen.

PRAYERS

My friend

Do you have a special friend?
I have....

Though you cannot see him,
he is very real. He is really there.
For he whispers in my ear 'It's alright'
when I scrape my knee on the playground.
He presses me back firmly – like the
strongest summer breeze – when I
want to strike out in temper.
He soothes me by his company when
a piece of news saddens me. He lets me
down gently when I face disappointment.
He is always there when I feel lonely,
and to share in my joys and triumphs.
He helps me to find the right words
like 'Sorry', 'Thank you' and 'Can I help?'
He never turns his back on me and
never breaks a promise.

He is the best friend anyone
could ever have.
He can be your friend, too –
if you ask him.

Keith Lockyer

Prayer

Thank you for
guiding me when I am lost,
caring for me when I am careless,
loving me when I am unlovable.

Help me to
understand when others are irritable,
share with those who have less than I,
protect those who are defenceless.

So that I
speak only words which are....
kind, true and necessary
and do to others as....
I would wish them to do to me.

Jill Jesson

New Year Resolutions

This year....
I will act as if everything I say or do can make a difference
This year....
I will do one thing to help at home every day,
This year....
I will say one kind, true thing to someone I do not like every week,
This year....
I will give something to someone who needs my help every month,
This year....
I will recycle everything I can throughout the year,
so that....
this year....
I will make a difference to the world.

Jill Jesson

Do all the good you can

Do all the good you can.
By all the means you can.
In all the ways you can.
In all the places you can.
At all the times you can.
To all the people that you can.
As long as ever you can.

John Wesley

A school creed

This is our school.
Let peace dwell here,
Let the room(s) be full of contentment,
Let love abide here,
Love of one another,
Love of mankind,
Love of life itself,
And love of God.
Let us remember
That, as many hands build a house,
So many hearts make a school.

Traditional (Used by a school in Canada)

Thank you for what we have

Help us to remember
other children around the world
who do not have enough food to eat
or water to drink
or clothes to wear.
Let us be thankful for all things that we have
and learn the importance of sharing.

Margaret Fairbairn

The Lord's name be praised

Hey, all you children,
Bless you the Lord!
All fathers and mothers,
Sisters and brothers,
Praise Him and magnify Him for ever!

All you deeps of the ocean,
Bless you the Lord!
All whales and porpoises,
Turtles and tortoises,
Praise Him and magnify Him for ever!

All field mice and larder mice,
Bless you the Lord!
All hedgehogs and moles,
Rabbits and voles,
Praise Him and magnify Him for ever.

Let everything that hath life
Praise the Lord!

Anonymous

Three things

Three things cannot be hidden.
the sun,
the moon,
and the truth.

Buddha

Thank you for music

A single note of music breaks
the silence in a lonely room.
but a melody, a song or a tune,
brings memories, thoughts and happiness.
Thank you, God, for beautiful music.

Anonymous

People who help us

We thank you God, for all the people
who have worked hard for the welfare
of children everywhere.

Anonymous

God is love

God is love, and those who live
in love live in God:
and God lives in them.

John 4.16.

Finding happiness

Give me a sense of humour Lord
Give me the grace to see a joke
To find some happiness in life
And pass it on to other folk.

Anonymous – Chester Cathedral

Lost and found

Is lost – gone forever?   Is found – here forever?
Is lost – never there?   Is found – always there?
Is lost – just forgotten?   Is found – simply remembered?

Just hidden?   Never hidden?
Do you care?   Yes, God cares.

Anonymous

Friends

Dear God, help us to understand that
friends are precious. May we always
be grateful for the company and
friendship of others.

Anonymous

Seeing good in others

Help us to see the
good in other people even though
they may not be our friends.
Help us to be kind when we are
tempted to be cruel.

Anonymous

Patience

Help us oh Lord to understand the
troubles of other people. Help us to
show patience and sympathy. Help
us to speak the truth at all times
even though it may not be easy.

Anonymous

Appreciation

Help us to appreciate the real treasures in life:
our family and friends – and all those who love us –
food and drink and good health,
schools and books and learning,
games and playing and holidays...
all the simple precious things that makes our lives special.

Margaret Fairbairn

Courage

God, give us courage to face
the difficult things in life.
May we be brave enough to do the
right thing when the wrong way
may be easier.

Anonymous

For all things fair

For flowers that bloom about our feet
For tender grass, so fresh, so sweet
For song of bird, and hum of bee
For all things fair we hear or see
Father in heaven, we thank Thee.

Anonymous

Growing up

We pray for the strength and courage to grow up ourselves;
to decide to leave behind those childish things that hold us back:
bad tempers, tantrums, jealousies and thoughtlessness.

John Cotton

The fair Earth

We thank thee, Lord, for this fair Earth –
The glittering sky the silver sea –
For all their beauty, all their worth,
Their light and glory come from thee.

Reverend George Cotton

A grateful heart

You have given me so much
Please give me one more thing
A grateful heart.

Anonymous

Open my eyes

Open my eyes to see what is beautiful
my mind to know what is true
and my heart to love what is good.

Anonymous

Shine upon us

O Lord Jesus Christ, who art the very
bright Sun of the world, ever rising,
never going down.
Shine upon us.

Erasmus

Self-knowledge

He who knows himself is enlightened
He who controls himself is powerful.

Confucius

Loved ones

God bless all those that I love;
God bless all those that love me;
God bless all those that love those that I love
And all those that love those that love me.

Anonymous

Helper, healer, friend

Jesus, friend of the friendless
helper of the poor
healer of the sick
whose life was spent in doing good.
let me follow in your footsteps.

Make me loving in all I do and say
Make me strong to do right
gentle with the weak
kind to all who are sad
so that I may be like you.

Anonymous

The Knight's prayer

God be in my head
    and in my understanding;

God be in mine eyes
    and in my looking;

God be in my mouth
    and in my speaking;

God be in my heart
    and in my thinking;

God be at my end
    and at my departing.

Anonymous

Prayer for the pet that died

You loved me with your whiskers
And I loved you
We shared so much together
You were my special friend
and I loved you.

Jonathan Davis (age 7)

The Gayatri mantra

Oh God, Creator and Life-Giver of the Universe;
Everywhere and in all things,
We meditate on your Splendour and Divine Light
And pray for purity of mind and knowledge of the Truth.

Traditional Hindu

Thank you

Thank you Lord, thank you,
Thank you for all I have seen, heard, received.
Thank you for the water that woke me up –
the soap that smells good,
the toothpaste that refreshes.

Thank you for the smile of my mother,
the hallo of my friends,
the kind words of a teacher.
Thank you for the tranquil night,
Thank you for the stars.
Thank you for the silence.
Thank you for life
Thank you Lord.

Abbe Michel Quoist

Different and special

Help us to remember
that we are all special in some way,
that we cannot all be the same
or be good at everything
or always come first.
Let us be thankful that we are all different
and all special.

Margaret Fairbairn

A child's prayer

Father, we thank Thee for the night
And for the pleasant morning light,
For rest and food and loving care,
And all that makes the world so fair.
Help us to do the things we should.
To be to others kind and good,
In all we do, in all we say,
To grow more loving every day.

Anonymous

Prayer for the planet

When we look around us at the vastness of the sea or the height of the mountains, we realise how small we human beings really are, and yet we manage to cause such mindless damage to our world – ripping up rainforests and hunting species to extinction.

We can only try to look after the bits of the earth on which we live. Our streets and gardens are hardly rainforests, but they are still beautiful: wild flowers push up between the paving stones, hedgehogs and foxes forage in gardens at night and kestrels hunt over the motorway verges.

For all this we want to say thank you and ask that you help us not to damage our environments in any way, but make them better places in which to live.

After all, we are only visiting this planet.

Jo Jennings

Index of the five main themes

Rules for living/growth

Stories: 7, 11, 13,18, 24, 30, 31, 32, 34, 36, 38, 40, 42, 44, 47, 49, 53, 54, 60, 62, 64, 66, 67, 69, 72, 74, 77, 79, 81, 83, 86, 90, 93, 96, 98, 102, 104, 106
Poems: 107, 108, 109, 110, 111, 112, 113, 114, 115
Songs: 150, 159, 160, 168, 176
Prayers: 178, 179, 181, 182, 183, 184, 184, 185, 186, 187

Family/friends

Stories: 13, 16, 18, 21, 24, 26, 28, 34, 36, 47, 53, 54, 62, 72, 77, 90, 93
Poems: 116, 117, 118, 119, 120, 121, 122, 123, 124, 125
Songs: 147, 148, 153, 154, 161, 162, 166, 170
Prayers: 177, 181, 182, 184, 186

Community

Stories: 24, 32, 38, 56, 67, 79, 81, 83, 98
Poems: 126, 127, 128, 129, 130, 131, 132, 133
Songs: 153, 156, 158, 162, 167, 170
Prayers: 179, 181, 182, 187

Environment and conservation

Stories: 49, 52, 54, 62, 69, 100
Poems: 134, 135, 136, 137, 138, 139
Songs: 164, 172, 174
Prayers: 183, 184, 187

Celebrations

Stories: 16, 32, 34, 40, 62, 83
Poems: 140, 141, 142, 143, 144, 145, 146
Songs: 152, 163, 174
Prayers: 180, 181, 183, 184, 186, 187

Index of Themes

Acknowledgements

The publishers gratefully acknowledge permission to reproduce the following copyright material:

© 1994 Ian Addis for 'The Atlantic Star', 'Becky's buttons', 'The little house that smiled', 'Marzipanned', 'A right to song', 'Runaway' (poem), 'Runaway' (prose), 'Snowdrops', 'That Christmassy feeling' and 'The watchers on the shore'; © 1994 Moira Andrew for 'Celebration' and 'Museum piece'; © 1994 Clive Barnwell for 'I want to say thank you', 'My friend', 'Why does an elephant grow so big' and 'Your ray of light'; © 1994 Ann Bryant for 'Kaleidoscope' and 'Spots'; © 1994 J. L. Carr for 'The Real Wonder or The boy who could flick peas into a milk bottle'; The Central Board of Finance of the Church of England for 'Feeding time' by Michael Proctor from No. 24 *Trustworthiness* in *First the Good News* (1982, Church House Press); © 1994 The Citizen Foundation for 'Wildlife' by Don Rowe; © 1994 John Cotton for 'Growing up', 'A pirate song' and 'Prince Siddhartha'; © 1994 David Coysh for 'Save the children'; © 1994 Jonathan Davis for 'Prayer for the pet that died'; Doubleday for 'The Asrai' from *A Chest of Stories for Nine Year Olds* (1991, Doubleday); © 1994 Gina Douthwaite for 'Birth' and 'Footpath from summer'; Edgell Communications for 'New pet' by Lois F. Pasley from *Poetry Place Anthology* (1983, Edgell Communications); © 1994 Anne English for 'The man who loved elephants' and 'Timothy's new ears'; 'No difference' by Shel Silverstein, © 1974 by Evil Eye Music Inc., by permission of Edite Kroll Literary Agency; © 1994 Margaret Fairbairn for 'Appreciation', 'Different and special' and 'Thank you for what we have'; David Fulton Publishers for 'Ben's flowers' by Ian Addis from *What Can the Matter Be? and other stories* (1992, David Fulton); Gill & Macmillan Publishers for 'Thank you' by Abbé Michel Quoist from *Prayers of Life* (1963, Gill & Macmillan); Victor Gollancz for 'The box' by Ann Cameron from *More Stories Julian Tells* (1986, Gollancz) and 'A pudding like a night on the sea' by Ann Cameron from *The Julian Stories* (1982, Gollancz); © 1994 Gwen Grant for 'Yan's first voyage'; HarperCollins Publsihers for 'The crowded house' by Robert Fisher from *Today Together - themes and stories* (1981, Evans Brothers), 'Crab's kingdom' by Tessa Morris-Suzuki from *All the Year Round* (1980, Evans Brothers) and 'The new house' by Gareth Owen from *Song of the City* (1985, HarperCollins); © 1994 Ian Henderson-Begg for 'Go take a walk', 'Praise the Lord' and 'You do it all for me'; David Higham Associates Ltd for 'The golden cat' by Eleanor Farjeon from *Silver, Sand and Snow* (1951, Michael Joseph) and 'Friendship' by Elizabeth Jennings from *The Secret Brother* (1966, Macmillan); © 1994 Mike Hoy for 'Books' and 'ST'; Instructor Books for 'Courage of life' by John F. Kennedy from *Poetry Place Anthology* (1983, Instructor Books) and 'Millions of people' by Jane W. Krows; © 1994 Andrew Jackson for 'The litter song'; © 1994 Jo Jennings for 'Prayer for the planet'; © 1994 Jill Jesson for 'New Year resolutions' and 'Prayer'; © 1989 Jean Kenward for 'New Year' from *Let's Celebrate* (1989, OUP); © 1994 Liz Lawman for 'Fair exchange is no robbery', 'Hazel', 'A moving story' and 'Promises, promises'; © 1994 Keith Lockyer for 'My friend'; Longman Cheshire for 'Blind girl' by Bill Scott from *Let's Enjoy Poetry* (1989, Longman Cheshire); © 1994 Wes Magee for 'At the end of a school day'; © 1994 Charles Marlow for 'Memorial', 'A special friend' and 'The tooth'; © 1994 Robin Mellor for 'I told a lie today', 'Seal song' and © 1993 Robin Mellor for 'Song of the refugee child' from *Welsh Rhubarb* (1993, Victoria Press); © 1994 Peter Morrell for 'Colours of the world', 'Don't throw grandad away' and 'Seal-song' (music); William Morrow & Co Inc. for 'The story of light' by Susan L. Roth (1990, Morrow Junior Books); © 1993 Brian Moses for 'Names' from *Somewhere to Be* (1993, WWF), © 1994 Brian Moses for 'Those were the days' from *Knock Down Ginger* (1994, CUP), 'Trees' from *Hippopotamus Dancing and other poems* (1994, CUP), 'The new lad' and 'Parent free zone'; Multicultural Services for 'An honest thief' by Timothy Callender and 'The crow and the sparrow'; NCEC for 'Time' by Pamela Scurr from *Fresh Voices* (1979, NCEC); Northampton County Council for 'One child' by Rachel Gray from *Born as the World Spins* (1976, NCC), 'Death of the elms' by Catherine Englishby from *Out of School into Print* (1988, NCC) and 'Getting ready for Christmas' by Robin Lester from *Primary Celebration* (1988, NCC); © 1990 Judith Nicholls for 'Rememberance Day' from *Dragonsfire* (1990, Faber & Faber); © 1994 Claude Oglethorpe for 'Raymond'; Oxford University Press for 'Truth' by Barrie Wade from *Conkers* (1989, OUP); © 1994 Gillian Parker for 'Greetings'; Ralph E. Pearce for 'A prayer' and 'A promise'; © 1994 Tom Quincey for 'Buried treasure', 'A place called Goodwill' and 'Today we're going to do poetry'; Reed Book Services for 'The miraculous Orange Tree' by Jamila Gavin from *The Orange Tree and other stories* (1979, Methuen); © James Reeves for 'Waiting' (Laura Cecil Literary Agency); © 1988 John Rice for 'Easter'; © 1994 Anita Marie Sackett for 'Gran's photo' and © 1989 Anita Marie Sackett for 'Our street' from *Junior Education* (August 1989, Scholastic); © 1985 Arthur Scholey for 'Villagers of Eyam' from *The Johnny Morris Story Book* (1985, BBC); © 1979 Robert Scott for 'The doko' from *The Orange Storyhouse* (1979, OUP); © 1994 Fred Sedgwick for 'Annunciation (Leonardo da Vinci)' and 'The Pharaoh addresses his god, the sun'; Simon & Schuster Young Books for 'Daniel's rabbit' by Fred Sedgwick from *Animal Poems* (1992, Simon & Schuster Young Books); © 1994 Ian Souter for 'Lost property', 'Mum', 'My Grandpa' and 'My heart beats'; © 1994 Sue Spooner for 'It's the little things that matter', 'The prayer', 'The promise' and 'The Last Supper'; Tamarind Ltd for 'Just a pile of rice' by Verna Wilkins and Gill McLean (1985, Tamarind); Roslyn Targ Literary Agency for 'Me and the baby brother' © Mary Stolz (1975, Open Court Publishing); Tinderbox Music for 'A handful of rice' by David Moses from *A Handful of Rice* (1992, Tinderbox Music), 'Help us to choose what to do and say' by David Moses from *20 Simple Songs and Games* (1993, Tinderbox Music), 'How it feels to be hungry' and 'I can be quiet' by David Moses © 1994 Tinderbox Music, 'I've got a friend called Albert' by David Moses © 1991 Tinderbox Music and 'Loulou the lollipop lady' by David Moses © 1983 Tinderbox Music; Wayland Ltd for 'The King's elephant' by John Snelling from *Buddhist Stories* (1986, Wayland); © 1994 John Welch for 'In, over, through, off'; © 1994 Jane Wright for 'Brothers and sisters' and 'It's today... isn't it?'; © 1994 Pauline Young for 'Conkers'.

Every effort has been made to trace copyright holders for material in this anthology and the publishers apologise for any inadvertent omissions.